WRITERS
EXPRESS

Daily Language Workouts

FEATURING
Daily MUG Shot Sentences
Weekly MUG Shot Paragraphs
Writing Prompts
Writing Topics
Show-Me Sentences

Level 5

Daily language and writing practice for
Grade 5

WRITE SOURCE®

GREAT SOURCE EDUCATION GROUP
a Houghton Mifflin Company
Wilmington, Massachusetts

www.greatsource.com

A Few Words About
Daily Language Workouts 5

Before you begin . . .

The activities in this book will help your students build basic writing and language skills. You'll find three types of exercises on the following pages:

MUG Shot Sentences There are 175 sentences highlighting **m**echanics, **u**sage, and/or **g**rammar (MUG). There's one sentence for every day of the school year. For the first 18 weeks, focused sentences usually concentrate on one skill per week. Then the sentences for the final 17 weeks present a mixed review of errors, and students are asked to correct several types of errors in each sentence.

MUG Shot Paragraphs There are 35 weekly paragraphs. During the first 18 weeks, the paragraphs, like the sentences, usually focus on one type of mechanics, usage, or grammar error. The paragraphs for the final 17 weeks offer a mixed review of editing skills based on skills covered during each week of sentences.

Daily Writing Practice This section begins with **writing prompts** presented on pages that you can photocopy or place on an overhead projector. The prompts include thought-provoking topics and graphics designed to inspire expository, narrative, descriptive, persuasive, and creative writing. A discussion of daily journal writing introduces the lists of intriguing **writing topics.** Finally, the **Show-Me sentences** provide starting points for paragraphs, essays, and a wide variety of other writing forms.

Authors: Pat Sebranek and Dave Kemper

Trademarks and trade names are shown in this book strictly for illustrative purposes and are the property of their respective owners. The authors' references herein should not be regarded as affecting their validity.

Great Source and **Write Source** are registered trademarks of Houghton Mifflin Company.

Printed in the United States of America

International Standard Book Number: 0-669-47435-5

6 7 8 9 10 -POO- 08 07 06 05

Table of Contents

Editing and Proofreading Marks

These symbols may be used to correct MUG Shot sentences and paragraphs.

Insert here.	∧	*them* take∧home
Insert a comma, semicolon, or colon.	∧, ∧; ∧:	Troy∧Michigan
Insert a period.	⊙	Mrs⊙
Insert a hyphen.	=∧	one=∧third cup
Insert a question mark or an exclamation point.	?∧ !∧	How about you?∧
Capitalize a letter.	/ (or) ≡	⫶toronto (or) toronto≡
Make a capital letter lowercase.	/	*h*/History
Replace or delete.	—— (or) ⌐	*cold* *hot* a h̶o̶t̶ day (or) a n̶o̶t̶ day (or) a h̶o̶t̶ day
Insert an apostrophe or quotation marks.	⌄' ⌄" ⌄"	Bill⌄'s ⌄"Wow!⌄"
Use italics.	————	Tracker

MUG Shot Sentences

The MUG Shot sentences are designed to be used at the beginning of each class period as a quick and efficient way to review **m**echanics, **u**sage, and **g**rammar. Each sentence can be corrected and discussed in 3 to 5 minutes.

MUG Shot Sentence Organizer

Name _____   Date_____

Corrected Sentence:

_____

_____

_____

Corrected Sentence:

_____

_____

_____

Corrected Sentence:

_____

_____

_____

Corrected Sentence:

_____

_____

_____

Corrected Sentence:

_____

_____

_____

Implementation and Evaluation

The first 18 weeks of MUG Shot sentences are focused sentences. The sentences for each week usually focus on one proofreading skill. The remaining 17 weeks of MUG Shot sentences provide mixed reviews of two or three different proofreading skills per sentence.

Implementation

On the days that you use MUG Shot sentences, we suggest that you have students **correct the sentence orally.** After you write the sentence on the board, be sure to read it aloud to be sure students understand the sentence. Write the corrections on the board as a volunteer provides them. (The student may use the proofreading marks on page iv.) Have the student explain his or her corrections and discuss the results. If you wish, then ask all students to write the corrected form in their notebooks.

You may also **write a sentence on the board** at the beginning of the class period. Allow students time to read the sentence to themselves. (Make sure they understand the sentence.) Then have students correct each MUG Shot in a space reserved for them in their notebooks (or on a copy of the "MUG Shot Sentence Organizer" provided on page 2 of this book). Students may be supplied with a copy of the "Editing and Proofreading Marks" on page iv as a guide for marking changes to their MUG Shot sentences. Be sure to read each sentence aloud before students begin. Then have students in pairs or as a class discuss their corrections. Also make sure that each student understands why the corrections were made.

Each Friday, review the MUG Shots covered for the week. You might assign the MUG Shot paragraph that contains errors similar to the type students have worked on for the week. (See page 75.)

Evaluation

If you assign sentences daily, evaluate your students' work at the end of each week. We recommend that you give them a basic performance score for their work. This performance score might be based on having each sentence for that week written correctly in their language arts notebooks. You might also have students reflect on their MUG Shot work in a brief freewriting at the end of the week, or have them correct one or two review sentences. Consider asking the students to submit sentences for this review activity.

Note: In the MUG Shot sentences showing corrections for run-on sentences, sentence fragments, and sentence combining, one possible correction is shown. However, there are often a number of possible answers that would also be correct.

WEEK 1: Beginning of the End

■ **End Punctuation**

Did you know there is one male calico cat for every 300,000

females

■ **End Punctuation**

Heat makes you sleepy in the afternoon and restless at night

■ **End Punctuation**

Oh, no, that plane is going to crash

■ **End Punctuation**

Why are all the Yellow Freight Company's trucks orange

■ **End Punctuation**

Watch out for that speeding car

WEEK 1: **Corrected Sentences**

■ **End Punctuation**

Did you know there is one male calico cat for every 300,000 females**?**

■ **End Punctuation**

Heat makes you sleepy in the afternoon and restless at night**.**

■ **End Punctuation**

Oh, no, that plane is going to crash**!**

■ **End Punctuation**

Why are all the Yellow Freight Company's trucks orange**?**

■ **End Punctuation**

Watch out for that speeding car**!**

WEEK 2: In Other Words

■ Comma (To Set Off Appositives)

Idaho the Gem State is also known for its potatoes.

■ Comma (To Set Off Appositives)

Colorado the Centennial State became a state in 1876.

■ Comma (To Set Off Appositives)

The hibiscus is the state flower of Hawaii the 50th state.

■ Comma (To Set Off Appositives)

America's favorite dessert ice cream was not an American invention.

■ Comma (To Set Off Appositives)

In 1994, Carla Garrett U.S. national women's champion lifted 275 pounds.

WEEK 2: **Corrected Sentences**

■ **Comma (To Set Off Appositives)**

Idaho, the Gem State, is also known for its potatoes.

■ **Comma (To Set Off Appositives)**

Colorado, the Centennial State, became a state in 1876.

■ **Comma (To Set Off Appositives)**

The hibiscus is the state flower of Hawaii, the 50th state.

■ **Comma (To Set Off Appositives)**

America's favorite dessert, ice cream, was not an American invention.

■ **Comma (To Set Off Appositives)**

In 1994, Carla Garrett, U.S. national women's champion, lifted 275 pounds.

WEEK 3: May I please introduce . . .

- **Comma (To Set Off Introductory Phrases and Clauses)**

Early in the 1974 baseball season Hank Aaron broke Babe Ruth's record by hitting his 715th home run.

- **Comma (To Set Off Introductory Phrases and Clauses)**

Even though some people think it was named after a baseball legend the Baby Ruth candy bar was actually named after President Cleveland's oldest daughter, Ruth.

- **Comma (To Set Off Introductory Phrases and Clauses)**

When airplane pilots fly in an easterly direction they fly at an odd-numbered altitude such as 29,000 feet.

- **Comma (To Set Off Introductory Phrases and Clauses)**

Flying at the altitude of 30,000 feet we knew we were headed west.

- **Comma (To Set Off Introductory Phrases and Clauses)**

Because of the growing popularity of snowmobiles fewer dogsleds are used in Alaska.

WEEK 3: **Corrected Sentences**

■ **Comma (To Set Off Introductory Phrases and Clauses)**

Early in the 1974 baseball season, Hank Aaron broke Babe Ruth's record

by hitting his 715th home run.

■ **Comma (To Set Off Introductory Phrases and Clauses)**

Even though some people think it was named after a baseball legend, the

Baby Ruth candy bar was actually named after President Cleveland's

oldest daughter, Ruth.

■ **Comma (To Set Off Introductory Phrases and Clauses)**

When airplane pilots fly in an easterly direction, they fly at an

odd-numbered altitude such as 29,000 feet.

■ **Comma (To Set Off Introductory Phrases and Clauses)**

Flying at the altitude of 30,000 feet, we knew we were headed west.

■ **Comma (To Set Off Introductory Phrases and Clauses)**

Because of the growing popularity of snowmobiles, fewer dogsleds are used

in Alaska.

WEEK 4: As I Said

■ Comma (To Set Off Dialogue)

"I've been waiting for hours" Amy complained. "Where have you been?"

■ Comma (To Set Off Dialogue)

"It's so hot" exclaimed Grandpa "that you could fry eggs on the sidewalk!"

■ Comma (To Set Off Dialogue)

"Money from other countries looks like play money to me" said Eustace.

■ Comma (To Set Off Dialogue)

Maria added "Multiplying large factors is easy if you know how."

■ Comma (To Set Off Dialogue)

"If you were in charge of naming new cars" said Mr. Jackson "how would you do it?"

WEEK 4: **Corrected Sentences**

■ **Comma (To Set Off Dialogue)**

"I've been waiting for hours," Amy complained. "Where have you been?"

■ **Comma (To Set Off Dialogue)**

"It's so hot," exclaimed Grandpa, "that you could fry eggs on the sidewalk!"

■ **Comma (To Set Off Dialogue)**

"Money from other countries looks like play money to me," said Eustace.

■ **Comma (To Set Off Dialogue)**

Maria added, "Multiplying large factors is easy if you know how."

■ **Comma (To Set Off Dialogue)**

"If you were in charge of naming new cars," said Mr. Jackson, "how would you do it?"

WEEK 5: Dividers

■ Comma (To Separate Adjectives)

Polar bears are strong clever animals and excellent powerful swimmers that have been spotted 100 miles from shore.

■ Comma (To Separate Adjectives)

The oldest tallest largest trees on earth are the pines, redwoods, and sequoias in the northwestern United States.

■ Comma (To Separate Adjectives)

Blackbeard was a tall bearded ferocious English pirate.

■ Comma (To Separate Adjectives)

Model T Ford cars were cheap popular vehicles.

■ Comma (To Separate Adjectives)

My dad likes to cook fancy complicated dinners once in a while.

WEEK 5: **Corrected Sentences**

■ **Comma (To Separate Adjectives)**

Polar bears are strong,clever animals and excellent,powerful swimmers that have been spotted 100 miles from shore.

■ **Comma (To Separate Adjectives)**

The oldest,tallest,largest trees on earth are the pines, redwoods, and sequoias in the northwestern United States.

■ **Comma (To Separate Adjectives)**

Blackbeard was a tall,bearded,ferocious,English pirate.

■ **Comma (To Separate Adjectives)**

Model T Ford cars were cheap,popular vehicles.

■ **Comma (To Separate Adjectives)**

My dad likes to cook fancy,complicated dinners once in a while.

WEEK 6: Organizing Your Thoughts

■ Colon, Comma (Items in a Series)

The men who signed the Declaration of Independence include the following John Hancock Thomas Jefferson Benjamin Franklin and John Adams.

■ Colon, Comma (Items in a Series)

If you can remember the acronym HOMES, you can remember the names of the Great Lakes Huron Ontario Michigan Erie and Superior.

■ Colon, Comma (Items in a Series)

The sports I like best are these basketball football and snowboarding.

■ Colon, Comma (Items in a Series)

Wisconsin is famous for the following cheeses cheddar Gouda and Edam.

■ Colon, Comma (Items in a Series)

Some of my favorite historic places are these the Statue of Liberty Williamsburg and the White House.

WEEK 6: **Corrected Sentences**

■ Colon, Comma (Items in a Series)

The men who signed the Declaration of Independence include the following: John Hancock, Thomas Jefferson, Benjamin Franklin, and John Adams.

■ Colon, Comma (Items in a Series)

If you can remember the acronym HOMES, you can remember the names of the Great Lakes: Huron, Ontario, Michigan, Erie, and Superior.

■ Colon, Comma (Items in a Series)

The sports I like best are these: basketball, football, and snowboarding.

■ Colon, Comma (Items in a Series)

Wisconsin is famous for the following cheeses: cheddar, Gouda, and Edam.

■ Colon, Comma (Items in a Series)

Some of my favorite historic places are these: the Statue of Liberty, Williamsburg, and the White House.

WEEK 7: Did You Know . . . ?

■ Semicolon

The United States once had a "King" in the White House President Gerald Ford's birth name before he was adopted was Leslie Lynch King, Jr.

■ Semicolon

The very first Olympic games took place in 776 B.C.E. at the foot of Mt. Olympus in Greece the first modern Olympic games were held in 1896 in Athens, Greece.

■ Semicolon

The Great Chicago Fire of 1871 lasted 27 hours it destroyed 17,450 buildings and killed 250 people.

■ Semicolon

The Chisholm Trail runs between San Antonio (Texas) and Abilene (Kansas) many "real" cowboys herded cattle along that trail in 1871.

■ Semicolon

Blowtorches of today can heat objects to over 14,000 degrees Fahrenheit diamonds will actually burn at that temperature!

WEEK 7: **Corrected Sentences**

■ **Semicolon**

The United States once had a "King" in the White House $_\wedge$ President Gerald
Ford's birth name before he was adopted was Leslie Lynch King, Jr.

■ **Semicolon**

The very first Olympic games took place in 776 B.C.E. at the foot of Mt.
Olympus in Greece $_\wedge$ the first modern Olympic games were held in 1896 in
Athens, Greece.

■ **Semicolon**

The Great Chicago Fire of 1871 lasted 27 hours $_\wedge$ it destroyed 17,450
buildings and killed 250 people.

■ **Semicolon**

The Chisholm Trail runs between San Antonio (Texas) and Abilene
(Kansas) $_\wedge$ many "real" cowboys herded cattle along that trail in 1871.

■ **Semicolon**

Blowtorches of today can heat objects to over 14,000 degrees Fahrenheit $_\wedge$
diamonds will actually burn at that temperature!

WEEK 8: Making Connections

- **Hyphen**

My well meaning mother makes me take some nasty tasting cough medicine at the first sign of a cold.

- **Hyphen**

The 13.5 ton bell in the clock tower of the Houses of Parliament in London is called Big Ben.

- **Hyphen**

In 1907, the first ever English author to receive the Nobel Prize for literature was Rudyard Kipling.

- **Hyphen**

Long playing records (you know, those old fashioned albums your grandparents have) were invented by Peter Goldmark.

- **Hyphen**

Lucy was an all American swimmer her last year in high school.

WEEK 8: **Corrected Sentences**

■ **Hyphen**

My well-meaning mother makes me take some nasty-tasting cough medicine at the first sign of a cold.

■ **Hyphen**

The 13.5-ton bell in the clock tower of the Houses of Parliament in London is called Big Ben.

■ **Hyphen**

In 1907, the first-ever English author to receive the Nobel Prize for literature was Rudyard Kipling.

■ **Hyphen**

Long-playing records (you know, those old-fashioned albums your grandparents have) were invented by Peter Goldmark.

■ **Hyphen**

Lucy was an all-American swimmer her last year in high school.

WEEK 9: Mine, All Mine

- **Apostrophe (In Possessives)**

  Because singer Frank Sinatras eyes were a beautiful blue color, he was called Ol' Blue Eyes by his fans.

- **Apostrophe (In Possessives)**

  Vandals broke all of the horns on the students locked-up bicycles.

- **Apostrophe (In Possessives)**

  The soft tissue of peoples vocal cords shrinks with age, making mens voices higher and womens voices softer.

- **Apostrophe (In Possessives)**

  Oklahomas dust storms in the 1930s blew away tons of soil.

- **Apostrophe (In Possessives)**

  The *T*'s burned into the steers hides tell you which ranch they belong to.

WEEK 9: **Corrected Sentences**

■ **Apostrophe (In Possessives)**

Because singer Frank Sinatra's eyes were a beautiful blue color, he was

called Ol' Blue Eyes by his fans.

■ **Apostrophe (In Possessives)**

Vandals broke all of the horns on the students' locked-up bicycles.

■ **Apostrophe (In Possessives)**

The soft tissue of people's vocal cords shrinks with age, making men's

voices higher and women's voices softer.

■ **Apostrophe (In Possessives)**

Oklahoma's dust storms in the 1930s blew away tons of soil.

■ **Apostrophe (In Possessives)**

The *T*'s burned into the steers' hides tell you which ranch they belong to.

WEEK 10: Attention, Please!

■ Quotation Marks

The landlord yelled up the stairs, Your tap dancing sounds like a demolition derby from down here! Try ballet!

■ Italics and Underlining

The three bears from the book The Three Bears must have liked porridge.

■ Quotation Marks

I think Writing Fantasies is one of the best chapters in my new handbook, and there's a lot of cool stuff in the Student Almanac section, too!

■ Quotation Marks

The slang expression ain't dates back to the 1700s and King Charles II of England.

■ Italics and Underlining

The Marx brothers starred in comic movies like A Night at the Opera.

WEEK 10: **Corrected Sentences**

■ **Quotation Marks**

The landlord yelled up the stairs, "Your tap dancing sounds like a demolition derby from down here! Try ballet!"

■ **Italics and Underlining**

The three bears from the book The Three Bears must have liked porridge.

■ **Quotation Marks**

I think "Writing Fantasies" is one of the best chapters in my new handbook, and there's a lot of cool stuff in the "Student Almanac" section, too!

■ **Quotation Marks**

The slang expression "ain't" dates back to the 1700s and King Charles II of England.

■ **Italics and Underlining**

The Marx brothers starred in comic movies like A Night at the Opera.

WEEK 11: First and Foremost

■ **Capitalization**

Mercury, the closest planet to the sun, is a little larger than earth's

moon.

■ **Capitalization**

A place called machu picchu is where an ancient Inca city was located in

peru.

■ **Capitalization**

Mount everest is the highest mountain in the world, but it is only 44

feet higher than K2, which is also called mount godwin austen.

■ **Capitalization**

The chinese language is spoken by the most people in the World, but

english is the most widespread language.

■ **Capitalization**

Brad says burger king and hardee's restaurants have the best fries on

the planet, but he's never tasted the food at juicy lucy's truck stop.

WEEK 11: **Corrected Sentences**

■ **Capitalization**

Mercury, the closest planet to the sun, is a little larger than *E*earth's

moon.

■ **Capitalization**

A place called *M*machu *P*picchu is where an ancient Inca city was located in

*P*peru.

■ **Capitalization**

Mount *E*everest is the highest mountain in the world, but it is only 44

feet higher than K2, which is also called *M*mount *G*godwin *A*austen.

■ **Capitalization**

The *C*chinese language is spoken by the most people in the *W*world, but

*E*english is the most widespread language.

■ **Capitalization**

Brad says *B*burger *K*king and *H*hardee's restaurants have the best fries on

the planet, but he's never tasted the food at *J*juicy *L*lucy's truck stop.

WEEK 12: Just One More Thing

■ Plurals

The man at the corner stand sells balloones, boxs of candy, and bunchs of flowers.

■ Plurals

Henry VIII had six wifes. One of his childs, Queen Elizabeth I, was credited with bringing about a golden age in England.

■ Plurals

At the picnic, we had platesful of food.

■ Plurals

Elephantes, whales, and cowes have calfs that require much care.

■ Plurals

Soloes are played by one musician, duets by two, and trioes by three.

WEEK 12: **Corrected Sentences**

■ **Plurals**

The man at the corner stand sells ~~balloones~~ *balloons*, ~~boxs~~ *boxes* of candy, and ~~bunchs~~ *bunches*

of flowers.

■ **Plurals**

Henry VIII had six ~~wifes~~ *wives*. One of his ~~childs~~ *children*, Queen Elizabeth I, was

credited with bringing about a golden age in England.

■ **Plurals**

At the picnic, we had ~~platesful~~ *platefuls* of food.

■ **Plurals**

~~Elephantes~~ *Elephants*, whales, and ~~cowes~~ *cows* have ~~calfs~~ *calves* that require much care.

■ **Plurals**

~~Soloes~~ *Solos* are played by one musician, duets by two, and ~~trioes~~ *trios* by three.

WEEK 13: Who's Counting?

■ **Numbers**

There are more than three and a half billion chickens in the world.

■ **Numbers**

20 of my classmates made the honor roll last quarter; that's ninety percent of the class!

■ **Numbers**

A female blue whale measuring one hundred and thirteen feet in length is the largest animal ever seen alive.

■ **Numbers**

Ty Cobb, who was among the first five players elected to the Baseball Hall of Fame in nineteen thirty-six, batted .320 in twenty-three straight years.

■ **Numbers**

Skip chapters four and five for now, but read pages forty and forty-one in chapter 6 for tomorrow.

WEEK 13: Corrected Sentences

■ Numbers

There are more than ~~three and a half~~ *3.5* billion chickens in the world.

■ Numbers

Twenty
~~20~~ of my classmates made the honor roll last quarter; that's ~~ninety~~ *90*

percent of the class!

■ Numbers

A female blue whale measuring ~~one hundred and thirteen~~ *113* feet in length

is the largest animal ever seen alive.

■ Numbers

Ty Cobb, who was among the first five players elected to the Baseball Hall

of Fame in ~~nineteen thirty-six~~ *1936*, batted .320 in ~~twenty-three~~ *23* straight years.

■ Numbers

Skip chapters ~~four~~ *4* and ~~five~~ *5* for now, but read pages ~~forty~~ *40* and ~~forty-one~~ *41*

in chapter 6 for tomorrow.

WEEK 14: See the Sea!

- ## ■ Using the Right Word

  I've heard tails of the see's rage that would turn you're hair white!

- ## ■ Using the Right Word

  If you poor most of the lemonade into you're glass, their will be fewer

  for me to drink.

- ## ■ Using the Right Word

  A storm window keeps the warm heir in you're house wear it belongs.

- ## ■ Using the Right Word

  It seams that the piccolo players always set next to the flutists in a

  orchestra.

- ## ■ Using the Right Word

  Ralphy untied all the nots he'd tied in his mom's apron strings, so she

  gave him a extra peace of cake.

WEEK 14: **Corrected Sentences**

■ Using the Right Word

                    tales   *sea's*   *your*
I've heard ~~tails~~ of the ~~see's~~ rage that would turn ~~you're~~ hair white!

■ Using the Right Word

        pour   *your*   *there*   *less*
If you ~~poor~~ most of the lemonade into ~~you're~~ glass, ~~their~~ will be ~~fewer~~

for me to drink.

■ Using the Right Word

                                    air   *your*   *where*
A storm window keeps the warm ~~heir~~ in ~~you're~~ house ~~wear~~ it belongs.

■ Using the Right Word

    seems   *sit*   *an*
It ~~seams~~ that the piccolo players always ~~set~~ next to the flutists in ~~a~~

orchestra.

■ Using the Right Word

                    knots
Ralphy untied all the ~~nots~~ he'd tied in his mom's apron strings, so she

        an   *piece*
gave him ~~a~~ extra ~~peace~~ of cake.

WEEK 15: One Plus One Equals One

- ## Combining Sentences

  The class of animals called Arachnida includes spiders. This class includes scorpions. It includes ticks as well.

- ## Combining Sentences

  The piece of amber contains a fossilized dragonfly. The piece of amber is golden. It is on the professor's desk.

- ## Combining Sentences

  The Swiss Alps are cut by many deep valleys. The valleys contain pretty towns and villages.

- ## Combining Sentences

  Greenland is the largest island on earth. Greenland was discovered in 982 C.E. by Eric the Red.

- ## Combining Sentences

  Canoeing on rivers in the spring can be dangerous. Sudden rainstorms can cause flash flooding.

WEEK 15: **Corrected Sentences**

- **Combining Sentences**

The class of animals called Arachnida includes spiders, This class includes scorpions, and It includes ticks. as well.

- **Combining Sentences**

golden   on the professor's desk
The piece of amber contains a fossilized dragonfly. The piece of amber is golden. It is on the professor's desk.

- **Combining Sentences**

The Swiss Alps are cut by many deep valleys, that The valleys contain pretty towns and villages.

- **Combining Sentences**

Greenland is the largest island on earth, and Greenland was discovered in 982 C.E. by Eric the Red.

- **Combining Sentences**

because
Canoeing on rivers in the spring can be dangerous, Sudden rainstorms can cause flash flooding.

WEEK 16: Yes or No

■ **Subject-Verb Agreement**

An African black mamba snake have been clocked slithering at 30 miles an hour.

■ **Subject-Verb Agreement**

Sidewinder rattlesnakes actually moves by jumping sideways along the ground.

■ **Subject-Verb Agreement**

Either the mamba or the blue racer are poisonous, but I can't remember which one.

■ **Subject-Verb Agreement**

I don't like chocolate or vanilla, but they remains the favorite ice-cream flavors for other people.

■ **Subject-Verb Agreement**

The highest bridge in the world were built 1,053 feet above Royal Gorge in Colorado.

WEEK 16: **Corrected Sentences**

■ **Subject-Verb Agreement**

An African black mamba snake ~~have~~ *has* been clocked slithering at 30 miles an hour.

■ **Subject-Verb Agreement**

Sidewinder rattlesnakes actually ~~moves~~ *move* by jumping sideways along the ground.

■ **Subject-Verb Agreement**

Either the mamba or the blue racer ~~are~~ *is* poisonous, but I can't remember which one.

■ **Subject-Verb Agreement**

I don't like chocolate or vanilla, but they ~~remains~~ *remain* the favorite ice-cream flavors for other people.

■ **Subject-Verb Agreement**

The highest bridge in the world ~~were~~ *was* built 1,053 feet above Royal Gorge in Colorado.

WEEK 17: Books . . . they

■ **Pronoun-Antecedent Agreement**

Young people enjoy Gary Paulsen's books because of its adventure and excitement.

■ **Pronoun-Antecedent Agreement**

Each of my aunts has their bookshelf full of paperback mystery stories.

■ **Pronoun-Antecedent Agreement**

In *Sarah, Plain and Tall,* Patricia MacLachlan tells the story of pioneers and its struggles on the prairie.

■ **Pronoun-Antecedent Agreement**

Every famous cowboy has their story, and I never grow tired of reading a new one.

■ **Pronoun-Antecedent Agreement**

If my friends Nick and Alonzo had his way, all the library books would be available on the Internet.

WEEK 17: **Corrected Sentences**

■ **Pronoun-Antecedent Agreement**

Young people enjoy Gary Paulsen's books because of *their* ~~its~~ adventure and

excitement.

■ **Pronoun-Antecedent Agreement**

Each of my aunts has *her* ~~their~~ bookshelf full of paperback mystery stories.

■ **Pronoun-Antecedent Agreement**

In *Sarah, Plain and Tall,* Patricia MacLachlan tells the story of pioneers

and *their* ~~its~~ struggles on the prairie.

■ **Pronoun-Antecedent Agreement**

Every famous cowboy has *his* ~~their~~ story, and I never grow tired of reading a

new one.

■ **Pronoun-Antecedent Agreement**

If my friends Nick and Alonzo had *their* ~~his~~ way, all the library books would

be available on the Internet.

WEEK 18: Something Is Missing

■ Sentence Fragment

John H. Glenn, Jr., the first American in orbit on February 20, 1962.

■ Run-On Sentence

The 2000 U.S. Census will be studied closely many changes occurred in the population between 1990 and 2000.

■ Run-On Sentence

A symphony is music written for an orchestra chamber music is written for a small group of musicians.

■ Sentence Fragment

More powerful cars than ever before in history.

■ Run-On Sentence

The Nelson-Atkins Art Museum in Kansas City has four giant shuttlecocks on its lawn it's as though a giant were playing badminton over the top of the museum.

WEEK 18: **Corrected Sentences**

- **Sentence Fragment**

became
John H. Glenn, Jr.,∧the first American in orbit on February 20, 1962.

- **Run-On Sentence**

The 2000 U.S. Census will be studied closely∧;many changes occurred in

the population between 1990 and 2000.

- **Run-On Sentence**

C
A symphony is music written for an orchestra. chamber music is written

for a small group of musicians.

- **Sentence Fragment**

There are m
∧More powerful cars than ever before in history.

- **Run-On Sentence**

The Nelson-Atkins Art Museum in Kansas City has four giant

I
shuttlecocks on its lawn. It's as though a giant were playing badminton

over the top of the museum.

WEEK 19: History of the Language

- ■ **Using the Right Word, Numbers, Quotation Marks (Special Words)**

   The oldest letter of the alphabet is the letter O, dating back two three thousand B.C.E.

- ■ **Comma (Items in a Series and To Set Off Introductory Phrases and Clauses), Subject-Verb Agreement**

   In our language things is always changing because of the way we talk write and use words from day to day.

- ■ **Using the Right Word, Apostrophe (In Contractions), Double Negatives**

   Sum slang words used in the 1960s arent never used much anymore.

- ■ **Numbers, Run-On Sentence, Spelling**

   Calligraphy is the art of beutiful handwriting it developed into an art form more than two thousand years ago.

- ■ **Comma (To Set Off Appositives), Capitalization, Sentence Fragment**

   Latin the language of the roman Empire the foundation of the english language.

WEEK 19: **Corrected Sentences**

■ **Using the Right Word, Numbers, Quotation Marks (Special Words)**

The oldest letter of the alphabet is the letter "O," dating back ~~two~~ ~~three~~ *to 3000*

~~thousand~~ B.C.E.

■ **Comma (Items in a Series and To Set Off Introductory Phrases and Clauses), Subject-Verb Agreement**

In our language, things *are* ~~is~~ always changing because of the way we talk,

write, and use words from day to day.

■ **Using the Right Word, Apostrophe (In Contractions), Double Negatives**

Some
~~Sum~~ slang words used in the 1960s aren't ~~never~~ used much anymore.

■ **Numbers, Run-On Sentence, Spelling**

Calligraphy is the art of ~~beutiful~~ *beautiful* handwriting. It developed into an art

form more than ~~two thousand~~ *2,000* years ago.

■ **Comma (To Set Off Appositives), Capitalization, Sentence Fragment**

Latin, the language of the *R*oman Empire, *is* the foundation of the *E*nglish

language.

WEEK 20: Animal Crackers

■ **Apostrophe (In Possessives), Adverb (Comparative/Superlative), Using the Right Word**

A hummingbirds bill works most well four sucking nectar from flowers.

■ **Plurals, Comma (Items in a Series), Hyphen**

Cave dwelling animals include certain kinds of bats cricketes and salamanderes.

■ **Adjective (Comparative/Superlative), Apostrophe (In Possessives), Using the Right Word**

A giraffes neck has no more bones then a humans—the bones are simply more larger.

■ **Apostrophe (In Possessives), Using the Right Word**

Parrots bills work like nutcrackers too open seeds and nuts.

■ **Subject-Verb Agreement, Rambling Sentence**

I know it are either the emu baby or the kangaroo baby that is called a joey and I can't remember which one it is and I need to know for a poem I'm writing.

WEEK 20: **Corrected Sentences**

■ **Apostrophe (In Possessives), Adverb (Comparative/Superlative), Using the Right Word**

A hummingbird's bill works ~~most well~~ best ~~four~~ for sucking nectar from flowers.

■ **Plurals, Comma (Items in a Series), Hyphen**

Cave-dwelling animals include certain kinds of bats, ~~cricketes~~ crickets, and ~~salamanderes~~ salamanders.

■ **Adjective (Comparative/Superlative), Apostrophe (In Possessives), Using the Right Word**

A giraffe's neck has no more bones ~~then~~ than a human's—the bones are simply ~~more~~ larger.

■ **Apostrophe (In Possessives), Using the Right Word**

Parrots' bills work like nutcrackers ~~too~~ to open seeds and nuts.

■ **Subject-Verb Agreement, Rambling Sentence**

I know it ~~are~~ is either the emu baby or the kangaroo baby that is called a joey, ~~and~~ I can't remember which one it is, and I need to know for a poem I'm writing.

WEEK 21: Animal Kingdom

- ### Comma (To Set Off Introductory Phrases and Clauses), Capitalization, Using the Right Word

  When a Horse and a Donkey have a foal together its called a Mule.

- ### Comma (Between Two Independent Clauses), Numbers

  The kangaroo has a thick, long tail, up to ninety-one centimeters (about 3 feet) and this helps the animal balance while leaping.

- ### Pronoun-Antecedent Agreement, Apostrophe (In Contractions), Subject-Verb Agreement

  If you ever saw a pike (a kind of fish), I think youd agree they look really mean.

- ### Subject-Verb Agreement, Plurals, Double Negatives

  There have never been no documented proof of healthy wolfs attacking human beings.

- ### Hyphen, Pronoun-Antecedent Agreement, Using the Right Word

  Two year old bears are as large as there parents when it leave home.

WEEK 21: **Corrected Sentences**

- ### Comma (To Set Off Introductory Phrases and Clauses), Capitalization, Using the Right Word

  When a *h*Horse and a *d*Donkey have a foal together*,*it's called a *m*Mule.

- ### Comma (Between Two Independent Clauses), Numbers

  The kangaroo has a thick, long tail, up to ~~ninety-one~~ *91* centimeters (about

  3 feet)*,*and this helps the animal balance while leaping.

- ### Pronoun-Antecedent Agreement, Apostrophe (In Contractions), Subject-Verb Agreement

  If you ever saw a pike (a kind of fish), I think youd*'* agree ~~they look~~ *it looks*

  really mean.

- ### Subject-Verb Agreement, Plurals, Double Negatives

  There ~~have never~~ *has* been no documented proof of healthy ~~wolfs~~ *wolves* attacking

  human beings.

- ### Hyphen, Pronoun-Antecedent Agreement, Using the Right Word

  Two*-*year*-*old bears are as large as ~~there~~ *their* parents when ~~it~~ *they* leave home.

WEEK 22: On the Map

- **Period, Capitalization, Sentence Problems ("Of" for "Have")**

  The oldest map of the World, a clay tablet from Babylon, might of been made around 600 b.c.e

- **Capitalization, Using the Right Word, End Punctuation**

  Can you believe that the base of the great pyramid of giza is a perfect square with the for sides resting on exact North-South and East-West lines

- **Comma (To Set Off Appositives), Apostrophe (In Contractions)**

  Mount Everest the tallest mountain in the world still grows at a rate of one centimeter (thats .394 inches) every year.

- **Comma (To Set Off Appositives and In Dates), Abbreviations**

  On May 29 1953 Sir Edmund Hillary an explorer from New Zealand and Tenzing Norgay a guide from Nepal became the first known people to reach the top of Mt Everest.

- **Capitalization, Comma (To Set Off Introductory Phrases and Clauses), Using the Right Word**

  According to the united states geological survey every year they're are more than an million little earthquakes around the world.

WEEK 22: **Corrected Sentences**

- **Period, Capitalization, Sentence Problems ("Of" for "Have")**

The oldest map of the *W*orld, a clay tablet from Babylon, might ~~of~~ *have* been

made around 600 ~~b.c.e.~~ *BCE*

- **Capitalization, Using the Right Word, End Punctuation**

Can you believe that the base of the *G*reat *P*yramid of *G*iza is a perfect

square with the ~~for~~ *four* sides resting on exact *N*orth-*S*outh and *E*ast-*W*est lines *?*

- **Comma (To Set Off Appositives), Apostrophe (In Contractions)**

Mount Everest *,* the tallest mountain in the world *,* still grows at a rate of

one centimeter (that *'* s .394 inches) every year.

- **Comma (To Set Off Appositives and In Dates), Abbreviations**

On May 29 *,* 1953 *,* Sir Edmund Hillary *,* an explorer from New Zealand *,* and

Tenzing Norgay *,* a guide from Nepal *,* became the first known people to

reach the top of Mt. Everest.

- **Capitalization, Comma (To Set Off Introductory Phrases and Clauses), Using the Right Word**

According to the *U*nited *S*tates *G*eological *S*urvey *,* every year ~~they're~~ *there* are

more than ~~an~~ *a* million little earthquakes around the world.

WEEK 23: More Maps

■ **Using the Right Word, Double Subjects, Apostrophe (In Contractions)**

When you study world history, youll learn that the first true cities they were the capitols of early civilizations, such as Ur in Mesopotamia.

■ **Numbers, Capitalization, End Punctuation, Run-On Sentence**

The pyramids of egypt are one of the 7 wonders of the world do you know what the other 6 are and what they have in common.

■ **Verb (Irregular), Double Subjects**

American explorer Richard E. Byrd (1888-1957) he becomed the first person to fly over both the North Pole and the South Pole.

■ **Comma (In Dates), Period, Sentence Fragment**

On July 20 1969 Neil A Armstrong the first man to walk on the moon.

■ **Subject-Verb Agreement, Capitalization, Run-On Sentence**

Robert Peary were the first explorer to arrive at the north pole in 1909 Roald Amundsen got to the south pole two years later.

WEEK 23: **Corrected Sentences**

■ **Using the Right Word, Double Subjects, Apostrophe (In Contractions)**

When you study world history, you'll learn that the first true cities ~~they~~

were the *capitals* ~~capitols~~ of early civilizations, such as Ur in Mesopotamia.

■ **Numbers, Capitalization, End Punctuation, Run-On Sentence**

The pyramids of *E*gypt are one of the *seven* 7 wonders of the world. *D*o you

know what the other *six* 6 are and what they have in common?

■ **Verb (Irregular), Double Subjects**

American explorer Richard E. Byrd (1888-1957) ~~he~~ *became* ~~becomed~~ the first

person to fly over both the North Pole and the South Pole.

■ **Comma (In Dates), Period, Sentence Fragment**

On July 20, 1969, Neil A. Armstrong *became* the first man to walk on the moon.

■ **Subject-Verb Agreement, Capitalization, Run-On Sentence**

Robert Peary *was* ~~were~~ the first explorer to arrive at the *N*orth *P*ole in 1909.

Roald Amundsen got to the *S*outh *P*ole two years later.

WEEK 24: World Maps

- ## Plurals, Numbers, Comma (To Set Off Introductory Phrases and Clauses)

Between the African countrys of Zimbabwe and Zambia the Zambezi River drops four hundred and twenty feet over Victoria Falls.

- ## Capitalization, Comma (To Keep Numbers Clear)

The great Barrier Reef off the Northeast coast of Australia is 1250 miles of beautifully colored coral.

- ## Capitalization, Numbers, Comma (To Set Off Interjections)

Yes the Sears tower is the tallest building in the United States with one hundred and ten stories that rise almost fifteen hundred feet (four hundred and fifty-seven meters) above the streets of chicago.

- ## Subject-Verb Agreement, Adjective (Comparative/Superlative)

The Uru people lives on the most high island in the world in the middle of Lake Titicaca in South America.

- ## Capitalization, Using the Right Word

Scientists have found fish skeletons in the middle of the Sahara dessert, which indicates that once their was an ocean their.

WEEK 24: **Corrected Sentences**

■ **Plurals, Numbers, Comma (To Set Off Introductory Phrases and Clauses)**

countries
Between the African ~~countrys~~ of Zimbabwe and Zambia, the Zambezi

420
River drops ~~four hundred and twenty~~ feet over Victoria Falls.

■ **Capitalization, Comma (To Keep Numbers Clear)**

G   *n*
The ~~g~~reat Barrier Reef off the ~~N~~ortheast coast of Australia is 1,250

miles of beautifully colored coral.

■ **Capitalization, Numbers, Comma (To Set Off Interjections)**

T
Yes, the Sears ~~t~~ower is the tallest building in the United States with ~~one~~

110   *1,500*
~~hundred and ten~~ stories that rise almost ~~fifteen hundred~~ feet (~~four~~

457   *C*
~~hundred and fifty-seven~~ meters) above the streets of ~~c~~hicago.

■ **Subject-Verb Agreement, Adjective (Comparative/Superlative)**

live   *highest*
The Uru people ~~lives~~ on the ~~most high~~ island in the world in the middle

of Lake Titicaca in South America.

■ **Capitalization, Using the Right Word**

Desert
Scientists have found fish skeletons in the middle of the Sahara ~~dessert~~,

there   *there*
which indicates that once ~~their~~ was an ocean ~~their~~.

WEEK 25: Map Time

- **Apostrophe (In Possessives), Using the Right Word**

  Swedens capitol city of Stockholm is built on many islands.

- **Using the Right Word, Comma (Between Two Independent Clauses), Capitalization**

  The country of Brazil decided to move it's capitol from the coastal city of Rio de Janeiro so the brand-new capital city of brasília was built far inland.

- **Adjective (Comparative/Superlative), Run-On Sentence**

  The baddest criminals of England used to be sent to Tasmania it's an island off the coast of Australia.

- **Numbers, Plurals**

  The 2 South American countrys of Guyana and Suriname are north of Brazil, have port citys for capitals, and border the Atlantic Ocean.

- **Italics and Underlining, Capitalization**

  The word "peninsula" comes from the latin paene for "almost" and insulae for "island."

WEEK 25: **Corrected Sentences**

■ **Apostrophe (In Possessives), Using the Right Word**

Sweden's ~~capitol~~ *capital* city of Stockholm is built on many islands.

■ **Using the Right Word, Comma (Between Two Independent Clauses), Capitalization**

The country of Brazil decided to move ~~it's capitol~~ *its capital* from the coastal city

of Rio de Janeiro, so the brand-new capital city of *B*rasília was built

far inland.

■ **Adjective (Comparative/Superlative), Run-On Sentence**

The ~~baddest~~ *worst* criminals of England used to be sent to Tasmania. *I*t's an

island off the coast of Australia.

■ **Numbers, Plurals**

The ~~2~~ *two* South American ~~countrys~~ *countries* of Guyana and Suriname are north of

Brazil, have port ~~citys~~ *cities* for capitals, and border the Atlantic Ocean.

■ **Italics and Underlining, Capitalization**

The word "peninsula" comes from the *L*atin <u>paene</u> for "almost" and <u>insulae</u>

for "island."

WEEK 26: Hand Signals

■ **Comma (In Direct Address and To Set Off Introductory Phrases and Clauses), Using the Right Word, Sentence Problems ("Of" for "Have")**

When you were riding your bike Shania you should of extended you're left arm straight out too signal a left turn.

■ **Comma (To Set Off Introductory Phrases and Clauses), Pronoun-Antecedent Agreement, Using the Right Word**

To signal a write turn on your bike extend your left arm out and bend them up at the elbow with your palm forward.

■ **Subject-Verb Agreement, Using the Right Word, Double Subjects**

Directors of television shows they signal that time are running out buy moving a index finger around in a circle.

■ **Apostrophe (In Possessives), Comma (To Set Off Appositives), Subject-Verb Agreement**

A tap of a finger on a television directors nose indicate that the performer or announcer the one on camera is right on time.

■ **Comma (To Set Off Introductory Phrases and Clauses), Subject-Verb Agreement**

When a television director rubs together the index finger and thumb of both hands the performer on stage are being signaled to slow down.

WEEK 26: **Corrected Sentences**

- **Comma (In Direct Address and To Set Off Introductory Phrases and Clauses), Using the Right Word, Sentence Problems ("Of" for "Have")**

  When you were riding your bike*,* Shania*,* you should ~~of~~ *have* extended ~~you're~~ *your*
  left arm straight out ~~too~~ *to* signal a left turn.

- **Comma (To Set Off Introductory Phrases and Clauses), Pronoun-Antecedent Agreement, Using the Right Word**

  To signal a ~~write~~ *right* turn on your bike*,* extend your left arm out and bend
  ~~them~~ *it* up at the elbow with your palm forward.

- **Subject-Verb Agreement, Using the Right Word, Double Subjects**

  Directors of television shows ~~they~~ signal that time ~~are~~ *is* running out ~~buy~~ *by*
  moving ~~a~~ *an* index finger around in a circle.

- **Apostrophe (In Possessives), Comma (To Set Off Appositives), Subject-Verb Agreement**

  A tap of a finger on a television director*'*s nose ~~indicate~~ *indicates* that the
  performer or announcer*,* the one on camera*,* is right on time.

- **Comma (To Set Off Introductory Phrases and Clauses), Subject-Verb Agreement**

  When a television director rubs together the index finger and thumb of
  both hands*,* the performer on stage ~~are~~ *is* being signaled to slow down.

WEEK 27: Colors, Signs, and Symbols

■ **Apostrophe (In Possessives), Plurals**

The different patterns and colores of Scotlands kilts (skirts) represent

different clans, or familys.

■ **Apostrophe (In Possessives), Combining Sentences**

In this country, brides dresses are often white. That color has symbolized

joy for many years.

■ **Quotation Marks, Capitalization**

Sequoyah created a written language for the cherokee people in 1821,

said mrs. henning.

■ **Capitalization, Comma (To Set Off Interruptions),
Apostrophe (In Possessives)**

Uncle sam in case you don't know was a real person whose famous

picture was used on the u.s. armys enlistment posters.

■ **Subject-Verb Agreement, Using the Right Word**

In our culture, putting you're index finger and thumb together to make a

"O" are a weigh of saying OK.

WEEK 27: **Corrected Sentences**

■ **Apostrophe (In Possessives), Plurals**

The different patterns and ~~colores~~ *colors* of Scotland's kilts (skirts) represent different clans, or ~~familys~~ *families*.

■ **Apostrophe (In Possessives), Combining Sentences**

In this country, brides' dresses are often white. *since* That color has symbolized joy for many years.

■ **Quotation Marks, Capitalization**

"Sequoyah created a written language for the Cherokee people in 1821," said Mrs. Henning.

■ **Capitalization, Comma (To Set Off Interruptions),**
   Apostrophe (In Possessives)

Uncle Sam, in case you don't know, was a real person whose famous picture was used on the U.S. Army's enlistment posters.

■ **Subject-Verb Agreement, Using the Right Word**

In our culture, putting ~~you're~~ *your* index finger and thumb together to make *an* ~~a~~ "O" ~~are~~ *is* a ~~weigh~~ *way* of saying OK.

WEEK 28: Light Colors

- ### Colon, Comma (Items in a Series), Period

  The acronym ROY G BIV stands for all of the colors of the rainbow red orange yellow green blue indigo and violet.

- ### Using the Right Word, Comma (To Set Off Interruptions), End Punctuation

  Is it true that ordinary white light which can be separated buy a prism is maid up of all the colors of the rainbow.

- ### Comma (To Set Off Appositives), Apostrophe (In Contractions), Quotation Marks (Special Words)

  The word *ultra* means beyond, so ultraviolet is a light beyond violet the last color of the spectrum; ultraviolet radiation cant be seen.

- ### Comma (Between Two Independent Clauses), Subject-Verb Agreement, Apostrophe (In Contractions)

  Objects reflects different parts of the light spectrum and thats why we see colors.

- ### Using the Right Word, Run-On Sentence

  A laser beam is photons of light traveling in the same direction such a beam can be powerful enough to burn a whole in medal.

WEEK 28: Corrected Sentences

■ **Colon, Comma (Items in a Series), Period**

The acronym ROY G. BIV stands for all of the colors of the rainbow, red, orange, yellow, green, blue, indigo, and violet.

■ **Using the Right Word, Comma (To Set Off Interruptions), End Punctuation**

Is it true that ordinary white light, which can be separated *by* a prism, is *made* up of all the colors of the rainbow?

■ **Comma (To Set Off Appositives), Apostrophe (In Contractions), Quotation Marks (Special Words)**

The word *ultra* means "beyond," so ultraviolet is a light beyond violet, the last color of the spectrum; ultraviolet radiation can't be seen.

■ **Comma (Between Two Independent Clauses), Subject-Verb Agreement, Apostrophe (In Contractions)**

Objects *reflect* different parts of the light spectrum, and that's why we see colors.

■ **Using the Right Word, Run-On Sentence**

A laser beam is photons of light traveling in the same direction. Such a beam can be powerful enough to burn a *hole* in *metal*.

WEEK 29: Signs and Symbols

- **Comma (To Separate Adjectives), Pronoun-Antecedent Agreement, Verb (Irregular)**

  The common everyday handshake beginned when men wanted to show each other we did not have weapons in our hands.

- **Subject-Verb Agreement, Run-On Sentence**

  You has to identify many traffic signs when you ride a bike the stop sign and the yield sign are two important ones.

- **Comma (To Keep Numbers Clear and Items in a Series)**

  Individuals businesses and organizations use more than 43000 ZIP (zone improvement plan) codes—numbers that never need commas!

- **Comma (Items in a Series and Between Two Independent Clauses), Capitalization**

  Leonardo da Vinci was one of the greatest italian painters and he was also a sculptor an architect and an engineer.

- **Capitalization, Comma (Items in a Series)**

  In his paintings, Pablo picasso used different shapes to represent people animals things and ideas.

WEEK 29: **Corrected Sentences**

- **Comma (To Separate Adjectives), Pronoun-Antecedent Agreement, Verb (Irregular)**

  The common*,*everyday handshake ~~beginned~~ *began* when men wanted to show each other ~~we~~ *they* did not have weapons in ~~our~~ *their* hands.

- **Subject-Verb Agreement, Run-On Sentence**

  You ~~has~~ *have* to identify many traffic signs when you ride a bike*;*the stop sign and the yield sign are two important ones.

- **Comma (To Keep Numbers Clear and Items in a Series)**

  Individuals*,*businesses*,*and organizations use more than 43*,*000 ZIP (zone improvement plan) codes—numbers that never need commas!

- **Comma (Items in a Series and Between Two Independent Clauses), Capitalization**

  Leonardo da Vinci was one of the greatest *I*talian painters*,*and he was also a sculptor*,*an architect*,*and an engineer.

- **Capitalization, Comma (Items in a Series)**

  In his paintings, Pablo *P*icasso used different shapes to represent people*,* animals*,*things*,*and ideas.

WEEK 30: U.S. History Dates

■ **Comma (To Set Off Introductory Phrases and Clauses), Capitalization**

Once the new american government was installed in 1789 George Washington was sworn in as the first President.

■ **Apostrophe (In Possessives), Verb (Irregular), Capitalization**

The Civil war beginned in 1861 when the Confederate's opened fire on Fort Sumter.

■ **Capitalization, Comma (In Dates)**

In the civil war, General Lee surrendered to General Grant at appomattox court house on April 9 1865.

■ **Verb (Irregular), Capitalization**

Rioting taked place when an African American student named James Meredith enrolled at the university of Mississippi in 1962.

■ **Numbers, Comma (To Set Off Introductory Phrases and Clauses)**

Upon entering the University of Georgia in 1962 Charlene Hunter-Gault became the first African American female student there in one hundred seventy-five years.

WEEK 30: **Corrected Sentences**

■ **Comma (To Set Off Introductory Phrases and Clauses), Capitalization**

Once the new *A*merican government was installed in 1789, George

Washington was sworn in as the first *P*resident.

■ **Apostrophe (In Possessives), Verb (Irregular), Capitalization**

The Civil *W*ar ~~beginned~~ *began* in 1861 when the ~~Confederate's~~ *Confederates* opened fire on

Fort Sumter.

■ **Capitalization, Comma (In Dates)**

In the *C*ivil *W*ar, General Lee surrendered to General Grant at

*A*ppomattox *C*ourt *H*ouse on April 9, 1865.

■ **Verb (Irregular), Capitalization**

Rioting ~~taked~~ *took* place when an African American student named James

Meredith enrolled at the *U*niversity of Mississippi in 1962.

■ **Numbers, Comma (To Set Off Introductory Phrases and Clauses)**

Upon entering the University of Georgia in 1962, Charlene Hunter-Gault

became the first African American female student there in ~~one hundred~~ *175*

~~seventy-five~~ years.

WEEK 31: U.S. History Facts

■ **Apostrophe (In Possessives), Verb (Irregular)**

Uncle Sams picture as we know it today was first drawed by cartoonist Thomas Nast.

■ **Apostrophe (In Possessives), Using the Right Word, Colon**

Thomas Nast also drew the mane political party symbols the Democrats donkey and the Republicans elephant.

■ **Comma (In Addresses), Capitalization, Run-On Sentence**

The first United States Congress met in new york city new york and in 1790, the capital moved to philadelphia pennsylvania and in 1800, the capital moved to washington D.C.

■ **Capitalization, Comma (In Dates), Using the Right Word**

President Lincoln's emancipation proclamation took affect on january 1 1863.

■ **Capitalization, Using the Right Word**

During the roaring twenties, women which cut there hair short and danced the Charleston were called "flappers."

WEEK 31: **Corrected Sentences**

■ Apostrophe (In Possessives), Verb (Irregular)

Uncle Sam's picture as we know it today was first ~~drawed~~ *drawn* by cartoonist

Thomas Nast.

■ Apostrophe (In Possessives), Using the Right Word, Colon

Thomas Nast also drew the ~~mane~~ *main* political party symbols : the Democrats'

donkey and the Republicans' elephant.

■ Comma (In Addresses), Capitalization, Run-On Sentence

The first United States Congress met in *N*ew *Y*ork *C*ity, *N*ew *Y*ork. ~~and~~ *I*n

1790, the capital moved to *P*hiladelphia, *P*ennsylvania. ~~and~~ *I*n 1800, the

capital moved to *W*ashington, D.C.

■ Capitalization, Comma (In Dates), Using the Right Word

President Lincoln's *E*mancipation *P*roclamation took ~~affect~~ *effect* on *J*anuary 1, 1863.

■ Capitalization, Using the Right Word

During the *R*oaring *T*wenties, women ~~which~~ *who* cut ~~there~~ *their* hair short and

danced the Charleston were called "flappers."

WEEK 32: Science Facts

■ **Sentence Fragment, Capitalization, Comma (To Set Off Appositives)**

Marie curie one of the first, noted female scientists born in poland in 1867.

■ **Run-On Sentence, Abbreviations, Comma (In Addresses)**

In 1849, Elizabeth Blackwell graduated from Geneva College of Medicine in Geneva NY she was the first woman in the U.S. to earn a medical degree.

■ **Colon, Capitalization, Apostrophe (In Possessives)**

Scientists divide the earths history into four eras precambrian, paleozoic, mesozoic, cenozoic.

■ **Comma (To Set Off Interruptions), Apostrophe (In Possessives), Numbers**

Scientist's believe that the earth's continents all 7 were once attached.

■ **Quotation Marks, Comma (Items in a Series), Capitalization**

According to my dictionary, one definition of the word *Precipitation* is hail mist rain sleet or snow.

WEEK 32: Corrected Sentences

- **Sentence Fragment, Capitalization, Comma (To Set Off Appositives)**

  Marie *C*urie, one of the first, noted female scientists, *was* born in *P*oland

  in 1867.

- **Run-On Sentence, Abbreviations, Comma (In Addresses)**

  In 1849, Elizabeth Blackwell graduated from Geneva College of Medicine in

  Geneva, ~~NY~~ *New York.* *S*he was the first woman in the ~~U.S.~~ *United States* to earn a medical degree.

- **Colon, Capitalization, Apostrophe (In Possessives)**

  Scientists divide the earth's history into four eras: *P*recambrian, *P*aleozoic,

  *M*esozoic, *C*enozoic.

- **Comma (To Set Off Interruptions), Apostrophe (In Possessives), Numbers**

  ~~Scientist's~~ *Scientists* believe that the earth's continents, all ~~7~~ *seven*, were once attached.

- **Quotation Marks, Comma (Items in a Series), Capitalization**

  According to my dictionary, one definition of the word *P*recipitation is "hail,

  mist, rain, sleet, or snow."

WEEK 33: Physical Science

- **Comma (Between Two Independent Clauses), Using the Right Word**

  "Kinetic energy" is the energy of moving things and "potential energy" is energy who could be used.

- **Apostrophe (In Possessives), Pronoun-Antecedent Agreement, Comma (Items in a Series)**

  George Washington Carver greatly helped the Souths economy when it developed products from such crops as peanuts soybeans and sweet potatoes.

- **Subject-Verb Agreement, Using the Right Word**

  Growth hormones in the write places makes it possible four a plant two bend toward the light.

- **Comma (To Set Off Interjections), Double Negatives, Run-On Sentence**

  A firefly lights up when the air tubes in its stomach are filled by oxygen and a pigment of fat no it's not no magic or electricity.

- **Using the Right Word, End Punctuation, Plurals**

  Don't you think you're science teacher all ready nose that a group of monkies is a *band*.

WEEK 33: **Corrected Sentences**

■ **Comma (Between Two Independent Clauses), Using the Right Word**

"Kinetic energy" is the energy of moving things‸and "potential energy" is

energy ~~who~~ *that* could be used.

■ **Apostrophe (In Possessives), Pronoun-Antecedent Agreement, Comma (Items in a Series)**

George Washington Carver greatly helped the South's economy when ~~it~~ *he*

developed products from such crops as peanuts‸soybeans‸and sweet potatoes.

■ **Subject-Verb Agreement, Using the Right Word**

Growth hormones in the ~~write~~ *right* places ~~makes~~ *make* it possible ~~four~~ *for* a plant ~~two~~ *to*

bend toward the light.

■ **Comma (To Set Off Interjections), Double Negatives, Run-On Sentence**

A firefly lights up when the air tubes in its stomach are filled by oxygen

and a pigment of fat. No‸it's not ~~no~~ magic or electricity.

■ **Using the Right Word, End Punctuation, Plurals**

Don't you think ~~you're~~ *your* science teacher ~~all ready~~ *already* ~~nose~~ *knows* that a group of

~~monkies~~ *monkeys* is a *band*?

WEEK 34: Science and Inventions

■ **Using the Right Word, Numbers**

A dessert is any area of the earth that gets fewer than 1 inch of rainfall every year.

■ **Apostrophe (In Possessives), Adjective (Comparative/Superlative), Comma (To Set Off Introductory Phrases and Clauses)**

The farther you go below the oceans surface the more dark and saltier it gets.

■ **Colon, Comma (Items in a Series), Spelling**

Thomas Edison invented the following the phonagraph the phonograph record the electric lightbulb and waxed paper.

■ **Pronoun-Antecedent Agreement, Using the Right Word**

Certain supernovas, or superstars, flare up in a big weigh; it may reach the brilliance of 200 million sons!

■ **Plurals, Subject-Verb Agreement**

Potatos consists mainly of starch, protein, and water.

WEEK 34: **Corrected Sentences**

- **Using the Right Word, Numbers**

  A ~~dessert~~ *desert* is any area of the earth that gets ~~fewer~~ *less* than ~~1~~ *one* inch of rainfall

  every year.

- **Apostrophe (In Possessives), Adjective (Comparative/Superlative), Comma (To Set Off Introductory Phrases and Clauses)**

  The farther you go below the oceans*'* surface*,*the ~~more dark~~ *darker* and saltier it

  gets.

- **Colon, Comma (Items in a Series), Spelling**

  Thomas Edison invented the following*:*the ~~phonagraph~~ *phonograph*,the phonograph

  record*,*the electric lightbulb*,*and waxed paper.

- **Pronoun-Antecedent Agreement, Using the Right Word**

  Certain supernovas, or superstars, flare up in a big ~~weigh; it~~ *way they* may reach

  the brilliance of 200 million ~~sons~~ *suns*!

- **Plurals, Subject-Verb Agreement**

  ~~Potatos consists~~ *Potatoes consist* mainly of starch, protein, and water.

WEEK 35: Potpourri

- **Subject-Verb Agreement, Sentence Fragment, Italics and Underlining**

  My friend and I wants to see the movie King Kong, a story about a big, hairy ape.   Actually attacks New York City!

- **Capitalization, Apostrophe (In Possessives), Hyphen**

  <u>Just tell me when we're dead!</u> and <u>hot and cold summer</u> are the childrens all time favorite books.

- **Using the Right Word, Adjective (Comparative/Superlative), Quotation Marks**

  I said, Anwar and Sumo are more better names for kittens then the two most popular ones, Tiger and Samantha.

- **Rambling Sentence, Numbers, Apostrophe (In Contractions)**

  I dont want to wear mink and I could wear my wool coat instead and did you know that forty mink had to die for that coat?

- **Pronoun-Antecedent Agreement, Comma (In Direct Address), Subject-Verb Agreement**

  Class we will write panagrams today. It is sentences that use all the letters of the alphabet.

WEEK 35: **Corrected Sentences**

- **Subject-Verb Agreement, Sentence Fragment, Italics and Underlining**

  My friend and I ~~wants~~ *want* to see the movie <u>King Kong</u>, a story about a big,

  hairy ape. *The ape* ^ ~~Actually~~ attacks New York City!

- **Capitalization, Apostrophe (In Possessives), Hyphen**

  Just *T*tell *M*me *W*when *W*we're *D*dead! and *H*hot and *C*cold *S*summer are the

  children's all-time favorite books.

- **Using the Right Word, Adjective (Comparative/Superlative), Quotation Marks**

  I said, "Anwar and Sumo are ~~more~~ better names for kittens ~~then~~ *than* the two

  most popular ones, Tiger and Samantha."

- **Rambling Sentence, Numbers, Apostrophe (In Contractions)**

  I don't want to wear mink. ~~and~~ I could wear my wool coat instead. ~~and~~

  *D*did you know that ~~forty~~ 40 mink had to die for that coat?

- **Pronoun-Antecedent Agreement, Comma (In Direct Address), Subject-Verb Agreement**

  Class, we will write panagrams today. ~~It is~~ *They are* sentences that use all the

  letters of the alphabet.

MUG Shot
Paragraphs

The MUG Shot paragraphs are a quick and efficient way to review **m**echanics, **u**sage, and **g**rammar errors each week. These paragraphs can also serve as excellent proofreading exercises. Each paragraph can be corrected and discussed in 8 to 10 minutes.

Implementation and Evaluation

For each set of MUG Shot sentences, there is a corresponding MUG Shot paragraph. The first 18 weeks of MUG Shot paragraphs focus on the one or two skills addressed in each week's sentences. The remaining 17 weeks of paragraphs feature a mixed review of proofreading skills addressing select editing and proofreading skills covered in each week's sentences.

Implementation

A MUG Shot paragraph can be implemented at the end of the week as a review or an evaluation activity. It may be done orally as a class. Otherwise you may simply distribute copies of the week's paragraph, read the paragraph aloud, and then have students make their corrections on the sheet. Students may use the "Editing and Proofreading Marks" in their handbooks or on page iv. Have students then discuss their changes (in pairs or in small groups). Afterward, go over the paragraph as a class to make sure that everyone understands the reasons for the changes. (You may want to refer to the corresponding MUG Shot sentences during your discussion.)

An Alternative Approach: Distribute copies of the MUG Shot paragraph along with the edited version. (They appear on the same page in your booklet.) Have students fold the edited version under, and then make their own changes. Once they are finished, they can unfold the paper and check their work.

Evaluation

If you use the paragraphs as an evaluation activity, we recommend that you give students a basic performance score for their work. This score should reflect the number of changes the student has marked correctly (before or after any discussion). The weekly score might also reflect the student's work on the corresponding MUG Shot sentences.

Note: In the MUG Shot paragraphs showing corrections for run-on sentences, sentence fragments, and sentence combining, one possible correction is shown. However, there are often a number of possible answers that would also be correct.

WEEK 1: Those Bony Cats

■ **End Punctuation**

Cats have 250 bones while humans have only 203 Wow, that's amazing Why do cats have so many bones Think about how cats move Have you ever seen cats walk fearlessly across a narrow ledge They leap from the stove to the refrigerator in one bound They can jump off a roof, crawl through tiny spaces, and curl up into perfect circles Their long tails help balance them when jumping or falling The 250 bones make all that movement possible Go, cats, go

WEEK 1: **Corrected Paragraph**

Cats have 250 bones while humans have only 203. Wow, that's amazing! Why do cats have so many bones? Think about how cats move. Have you ever seen cats walk fearlessly across a narrow ledge? They leap from the stove to the refrigerator in one bound. They can jump off a roof, crawl through tiny spaces, and curl up into perfect circles. Their long tails help balance them when jumping or falling. The 250 bones make all that movement possible. Go, cats, go!

WEEK 2: Yum!

■ Comma (To Set Off Appositives)

Ice cream America's favorite dessert is not an American invention. The first ice cream was made 2,000 years ago in China home to one of the world's oldest civilizations. In the past, cream was mixed with a freezing combination of ice or snow and coarse salt. Today, gelatin a jellylike substance is added to hold ice cream together. Then it's mixed and pasteurized. Giraldo's an ice-cream store in my neighborhood is where I like to enjoy my favorite treat a strawberry pistachio ice-cream sundae.

WEEK 2: **Corrected Paragraph**

Ice cream, America's favorite dessert, is not an American invention. The first ice cream was made 2,000 years ago in China, home to one of the world's oldest civilizations. In the past, cream was mixed with a freezing combination of ice or snow and coarse salt. Today, gelatin, a jellylike substance, is added to hold ice cream together. Then it's mixed and pasteurized. Giraldo's, an ice-cream store in my neighborhood, is where I like to enjoy my favorite treat, a strawberry pistachio ice-cream sundae.

WEEK 3: Race Against Death

■ Comma (To Set Off Introductory Phrases and Clauses)

In the harsh winter of 1925 a deadly disease struck Nome, Alaska. When the town's doctor realized the disease was diphtheria he called for medicine. Because it was winter the ports were frozen shut, and the roads were blocked with snow. Men driving dogsleds brought the medicine the 674 miles from Anchorage. Through blizzards and temperatures reaching -100° Fahrenheit the dogsleds mushed onward. In five days a team reached Nome, and many people's lives were saved.

WEEK 3: **Corrected Paragraph**

In the harsh winter of 1925, a deadly disease struck Nome, Alaska. When the town's doctor realized the disease was diphtheria, he called for medicine. Because it was winter, the ports were frozen shut, and the roads were blocked with snow. Men driving dogsleds brought the medicine the 674 miles from Anchorage. Through blizzards and temperatures reaching -100° Fahrenheit, the dogsleds mushed onward. In five days, a team reached Nome, and many people's lives were saved.

WEEK 4: Rich Fertilizer

■ Comma (To Set Off Dialogue)

"Have you heard about the countries in Europe that have decided to use one kind of money?" asked Andy.

"Yes" said Rachel. "The new money is called the euro."

"I just read about what will happen to the leftover money" said Andy.

"Well, don't keep me in suspense" Rachel replied.

"The Germans are shredding their old money" explained Andy "and turning it into compost, the fertilizer you put on gardens."

"I guess they'll have some really rich soil" said Rachel.

WEEK 4: **Corrected Paragraph**

"Have you heard about the countries in Europe that have decided to use one kind of money?" asked Andy.

"Yes," said Rachel. "The new money is called the euro."

"I just read about what will happen to the leftover money," said Andy.

"Well, don't keep me in suspense," Rachel replied.

"The Germans are shredding their old money," explained Andy, "and turning it into compost, the fertilizer you put on gardens."

"I guess they'll have some really rich soil," said Rachel

WEEK 5: Proud Giants

■ **Comma (To Separate Adjectives)**

The ancient giant sequoias of California are 2,000 to 4,000 years old. These trees often live long healthy lives. It helps that their wood is light, coarse, and fire-resistant. Also destructive disease-carrying insects don't bother sequoias. Finally, tough laws have been passed to protect these ancient priceless trees from humans. Long long ago these beautiful old giants could be found all over the Northwest.

WEEK 5: **Corrected Paragraph**

The ancient, giant sequoias of California are 2,000 to 4,000 years old. These trees often live long, healthy lives. It helps that their wood is light, coarse, and fire-resistant. Also destructive, disease-carrying insects don't bother sequoias. Finally, tough laws have been passed to protect these ancient, priceless trees from humans. Long, long ago these beautiful, old giants could be found all over the Northwest.

WEEK 6: Busy Ben

■ Colon, Comma (Items in a Series)

Ben Franklin was a founder of our country. He was known for the following traits common sense wisdom hard work intelligence and a sense of humor. Franklin had many different jobs and careers during his long lifetime. Here are a few of them paperboy printer scientist diplomat and writer. Franklin was also a dreamer and an inventor. His most famous inventions are as follows the Franklin stove the lightning rod and bifocal glasses. We still use all of these things today.

WEEK 6: **Corrected Paragraph**

Ben Franklin was a founder of our country. He was known for the following traits: common sense, wisdom, hard work, intelligence, and a sense of humor. Franklin had many different jobs and careers during his long lifetime. Here are a few of them: paperboy, printer, scientist, diplomat, and writer. Franklin was also a dreamer and an inventor. His most famous inventions are as follows: the Franklin stove, the lightning rod, and bifocal glasses. We still use all of these things today.

WEEK 7: President with a Wheelchair

■ **Semicolon**

Franklin Roosevelt was elected president four times. Many Americans did not know that Roosevelt had a serious handicap he was paralyzed from the waist down. In 1921, Roosevelt got polio it left him crippled. Newspapers protected Roosevelt's privacy. Pictures rarely showed him in a wheelchair they almost always showed him from the waist up. Roosevelt was strong and determined. His handicap did not stop him he became one of the most admired presidents of all time.

WEEK 7: **Corrected Paragraph**

Franklin Roosevelt was elected president four times. Many Americans did not know that Roosevelt had a serious handicap; he was paralyzed from the waist down. In 1921, Roosevelt got polio; it left him crippled. Newspapers protected Roosevelt's privacy. Pictures rarely showed him in a wheelchair; they almost always showed him from the waist up. Roosevelt was strong and determined. His handicap did not stop him; he became one of the most admired presidents of all time.

WEEK 8: The Force

■ **Hyphen**

Are you a long suffering fan who waits for hours in line to see the latest movie? In a movie, which of the following do you like the most: fast paced action, computer made creatures, or high tech battle scenes? Do you prefer science fiction adventures, spine tingling thrillers, or those real-life, heart tugging dramas? Whether you prefer side splitting comedy, goose bumps, or animated cartoons, movies provide a world of entertainment.

WEEK 8: **Corrected Paragraph**

Are you a long-suffering fan who waits for hours in line to see the latest movie? In a movie, which of the following do you like the most: fast-paced action, computer-made creatures, or high-tech battle scenes? Do you prefer science-fiction adventures, spine-tingling thrillers, or those real-life, heart-tugging dramas? Whether you prefer side-splitting comedy, goose bumps, or animated cartoons, movies provide a world of entertainment.

WEEK 9: Goin' to California

■ Apostrophe (In Possessives)

In Oklahoma in the 1930s, my great-uncle Amos farm was wiped out by drought and dust storms. Many of Oklahomas, Texas, Kansas, Colorados, New Mexicos, and Arkansas farmlands dried up and blew away. The farmers methods of farming in those areas led to massive soil erosion. They couldn't make a living anymore. Uncle Amos and Aunt Ednas family headed west. That's how one part of my family ended up in California.

WEEK 9: **Corrected Paragraph**

In Oklahoma in the 1930s, my great-uncle Amos's farm was wiped out by drought and dust storms. Many of Oklahoma's, Texas's, Kansas's, Colorado's, New Mexico's, and Arkansas's farmlands dried up and blew away. The farmers' methods of farming in those areas led to massive soil erosion. They couldn't make a living anymore. Uncle Amos and Aunt Edna's family headed west. That's how one part of my family ended up in California.

WEEK 10: Spare-Time Choices

■ Quotation Marks, Italics and Underlining

The Museum of Television and Radio in New York has 35,000 tapes of TV shows. My friend Joe said, I'd like being locked in there for a weekend, watching reruns of favorite shows. The word *fan* is short for "fanatic." Joe is a TV fanatic, but I'd rather read The Westing Game again or the chapter Ways to Make Anything Disappear from my book on magic. Besides, if Joe were locked in a museum, he'd probably yell, Let me out of here! the first time he had a snack attack.

WEEK 10: **Corrected Paragraph**

The Museum of Television and Radio in New York has 35,000 tapes of TV shows. My friend Joe said, ⁶⁶I'd like being locked in there for a weekend, watching reruns of favorite shows.⁹⁹ The word *fan* is short for "fanatic." Joe is a TV fanatic, but I'd rather read <u>The Westing Game</u> again or the chapter ⁶⁶Ways to Make Anything Disappear⁹⁹ from my book on magic. Besides, if Joe were locked in a museum, he'd probably yell, ⁶⁶Let me out of here!⁹⁹ the first time he had a snack attack.

WEEK 11: The Mighty Incas

■ **Capitalization**

For more than 300 years, the incas lived in the cliffs and valleys of the andes mountains in south America. Their kingdom stretched 2,500 miles from what is now ecuador on the north to chile in the south— about the distance between new york city and miami, florida. The spanish explorer francisco pizarro came along in 1532. his goal was to conquer the incas and convert them to christianity. The Incas thought Pizarro and his men were Gods. Through trickery, violence, and disease, the empire of the great incas was destroyed.

WEEK 11: **Corrected Paragraph**

For more than 300 years, the *I*ncas lived in the cliffs and valleys of the *A*ndes *M*ountains in *S*outh America. Their kingdom stretched 2,500 miles from what is now *E*cuador on the north to *C*hile in the south— about the distance between *N*ew *Y*ork *C*ity and *M*iami, *F*lorida. The *S*panish explorer *F*rancisco *P*izarro came along in 1532. *H*is goal was to conquer the *I*ncas and convert them to *C*hristianity. The Incas thought Pizarro and his men were *g*ods. Through trickery, violence, and disease, the empire of the great *I*ncas was destroyed.

WEEK 12: First Picnic

■ **Plurals**

In early spring, when skys are sunny, my family goes on its first picnic. I mix four cupsful of orange juice, two cupful of milk, two spoonsfuls of vanilla, and some water and sugar. Then I add two traysful of ice cubes and put it all into the blender (with the lid on). We pack bunchs of carrots and celery, a couple loafs of bread, sliced meat, mustard, cheese, potato chips, and watermelon. We take plates, napkins, silverware, and knifes. The armys of ants never spoil our picnices. We eat inside our camper.

WEEK 12: **Corrected Paragraph**

In early spring, when ~~skys~~ *skies* are sunny, my family goes on its first picnic. I mix four ~~cupsful~~ *cupfuls* of orange juice, two ~~cupful~~ *cupfuls* of milk, two ~~spoonsfuls~~ *spoonfuls* of vanilla, and some water and sugar. Then I add two ~~traysful~~ *trayfuls* of ice cubes and put it all into the blender (with the lid on). We pack ~~bunchs~~ *bunches* of carrots and celery, a couple ~~loafs~~ *loaves* of bread, sliced meat, mustard, cheese, potato chips, and watermelon. We take plates, napkins, silverware, and ~~knifes~~ *knives*. The ~~armys~~ *armies* of ants never spoil our ~~picnices~~ *picnics*. We eat inside our camper.

WEEK 13: Who's on First?

■ **Numbers**

Ty Cobb scored two thousand two hundred and forty-six runs during his long baseball career. Cobb is number 1 in batting average and runs and number 2 in hits. He wasn't a great home-run hitter though. No one has beaten Hank Aaron's record of seven hundred fifty-five career home runs. In nineteen hundred ninety-eight, Mark McGwire set a one-year home-run record by hitting seventy balls out of the park.

WEEK 13: **Corrected Paragraph**

Ty Cobb scored ~~two thousand two hundred and forty-six~~ *2,246* runs during his long baseball career. Cobb is number ~~1~~ *one* in batting average and runs and number ~~2~~ *two* in hits. He wasn't a great home-run hitter though. No one has beaten Hank Aaron's record of ~~seven hundred fifty-five~~ *755* career home runs. In ~~nineteen hundred ninety-eight~~ *1998*, Mark McGwire set a one-year home-run record by hitting ~~seventy~~ *70* balls out of the park.

WEEK 14: Our Wet, Wet Planet

■ Using the Right Word

Did you no that two-thirds of the earth is covered buy water? My

teacher learned me that in second grade. The oceans of the world are

the Atlantic, Pacific, Indian, Arctic, and Antarctic. There all connected.

Your probably familiar with the Mediterranean Sea, but have you herd of

the Aral See?   If you've ever scene a ocean, you may think it would

make alot more cents to name our planet "Water" instead of "Earth."

WEEK 14: **Corrected Paragraph**

know
Did you ~~no~~ that two-thirds of the earth is covered ~~buy~~ water? My
by

taught
teacher ~~learned~~ me that in second grade. The oceans of the world are

They're
the Atlantic, Pacific, Indian, Arctic, and Antarctic. ~~There~~ all connected.

You're   *heard*
~~Your~~ probably familiar with the Mediterranean Sea, but have you ~~herd~~ of

Sea   *seen an*
the Aral ~~See~~?   If you've ever ~~scene~~ ~~a~~ ocean, you may think it would

a lot   *sense*
make ~~alot~~ more ~~cents~~ to name our planet "Water" instead of "Earth."

WEEK 15: Greenland Has Room to Grow

■ Combining Sentences

Greenland is an island. Greenland is the largest island in the world. Its 55,500 inhabitants govern themselves. The country has close ties to Denmark. Nuuk was founded in 1721. It is the capital of Greenland. It is the largest city in Greenland. It has 12,000 people. Children are taught Greenlandic. Greenlandic is an Inuit language. They are also taught Danish.

WEEK 15: **Corrected Paragraph** *(Answers may vary.)*

Greenland is ~~an island. Greenland is~~ the largest island in the world. Its 55,500 inhabitants govern themselves, although The country has close ties to Denmark. Nuuk was founded in 1721, the capital of Greenland, and ~~It is the capital of Greenland.~~ It is the largest city in Greenland. It has 12,000 people. Children are taught Greenlandic, ~~Greenlandic is~~ an Inuit language, and They are also taught Danish.

WEEK 16: Creepy Crawlies

■ **Subject-Verb Agreement**

Some reptiles, like giant tortoises, lives longer than human beings. There be some tortoises more than 100 years old. When you think of reptiles, however, you probably thinks of rattlesnakes and cobras. These snakes is poisonous, all right, but many kinds of snakes is not. Some people chooses snakes for pets. Other people don't like the idea of warming up to a cold-blooded snake.

WEEK 16: **Corrected Paragraph**

Some reptiles, like giant tortoises, ~~lives~~ *live* longer than human beings. There ~~be~~ *are* some tortoises more than 100 years old. When you think of reptiles, however, you probably ~~thinks~~ *think* of rattlesnakes and cobras. These snakes ~~is~~ *are* poisonous, all right, but many kinds of snakes ~~is~~ *are* not. Some people ~~chooses~~ *choose* snakes for pets. Other people don't like the idea of warming up to a cold-blooded snake.

WEEK 17: Literature and Reading

■ Pronoun-Antecedent Agreement

Boys like to read Gary Paulsen's books because of its exciting story lines and short lengths. Paulsen receives 200 to 400 letters every day from boys who enjoy their writing. Paulsen's book *Soldier's Heart* is 102 pages long and tells the true story of a 16-year-old Minnesota boy who left their family's farm to join the Union army. The boy learns about war and their many hard truths.

WEEK 17: **Corrected Paragraph**

Boys like to read Gary Paulsen's books because of ~~its~~ *their* exciting story lines and short lengths. Paulsen receives 200 to 400 letters every day from boys who enjoy ~~their~~ *his* writing. Paulsen's book *Soldier's Heart* is 102 pages long and tells the true story of a 16-year-old Minnesota boy who left ~~their~~ *his* family's farm to join the Union army. The boy learns about war and ~~their~~ *its* many hard truths.

WEEK 18: How Much Horsepower?

■ Sentence Fragment and Run-On Sentence

Cars have more horsepower than ever that's a fact. Some cars have as much as 300 horsepower this is more than some heavy trucks. The average car. Had 160 horsepower in 1998. That's 60 percent more than 20 years ago some people wonder if that much horsepower is necessary many drivers love power.

WEEK 18: **Corrected Paragraph** *(Answers may vary.)*

Cars have more horsepower than ever. *T*hat's a fact. Some cars have as much as 300 horsepower. *T*his is more than some heavy trucks. The average car *h*ad 160 horsepower in 1998. That's 60 percent more than 20 years ago. *S*ome people wonder if that much horsepower is necessary. *M*any drivers love power.

WEEK 19: Beautiful Writing

■ **Quotation Marks (Special Words), Using the Right Word, Capitalization, Comma (To Set Off Introductory Phrases and Clauses)**

The word *calligraphy* means beautiful writing in greek. When you think of calligraphy you probably think of the fancy writing that you see on wedding announcements. In islamic countries and in india, china, and japan, calligraphy is art. In china and in other countries calligraphy is often combined with quite nature seens on long scrolls.

WEEK 19: **Corrected Paragraph**

The word *calligraphy* means ""beautiful writing"" in Greek. When you think of calligraphy, you probably think of the fancy writing that you see on wedding announcements. In Islamic countries, and in India, China, and Japan, calligraphy is art. In China and in other countries, calligraphy is often combined with ~~quite~~ quiet nature ~~seens~~ scenes on long scrolls.

WEEK 20: Flying Mammals

- **Subject-Verb Agreement, Rambling Sentence, Hyphen, Apostrophe (In Possessives), Adverb (Comparative/Superlative)**

Bats has gotten a bad rap over the years. They are associated with Halloween and horror movies. The hours they keep don't help their reputation. They sleeps all day and comes out at night to hunt. Bats have their own sonar system and they send out high pitched sounds as they fly and their big ears picks up the echoes and then they know how to navigate in the dark. A bats diet consist of lots of mosquitoes. Maybe people should like bats more better than they do.

WEEK 20: **Corrected Paragraph**

Bats ~~has~~ *have* gotten a bad rap over the years. They are associated with Halloween and horror movies. The hours they keep don't help their reputation. They ~~sleeps~~ *sleep* all day and ~~comes~~ *come* out at night to hunt. Bats have their own sonar system, and they send out high-pitched sounds as they fly. ~~and~~ Their big ears ~~picks~~ *pick* up the echoes, and then they know how to navigate in the dark. A bat's diet ~~consist~~ *consists* of lots of mosquitoes. Maybe people should like bats ~~more~~ better than they do.

WEEK 21: The Bear Truth

■ **Capitalization, Using the Right Word, Apostrophe (In Contractions), Double Negatives**

Bears are found in north America, south America, Europe, and asia. The largest brown bare in the world is an United States Citizen. He or she lives on kodiak island in the gulf of Alaska. Kodiak bears stand tall (up to 10 feet) and may way almost 900 pounds. Despite their size and power, most bears dont want to mess with no people, and thats just fine with most people.

WEEK 21: **Corrected Paragraph**

Bears are found in *N*orth America, *S*outh America, Europe, and *A*sia. The largest brown ~~bare~~ *bear* in the world is ~~an~~ *a* United States *C*itizen. He or she lives on *K*odiak *I*sland in the *G*ulf of Alaska. Kodiak bears stand tall (up to 10 feet) and may ~~way~~ *weigh* almost 900 pounds. Despite their size and power, most bears don't want to mess with ~~no~~ people, and that's just fine with most people.

WEEK 22: Mt. Everest Mystery

- ### End Punctuation, Sentence Problems ("Of" for "Have"), Using the Right Word, Comma (To Set Off Appositives and In Dates)

Were Sir Edmund Hillary and Tenzing Norgay his guide the first to reach the top of Mt. Everest. They reached the summit on May 29 1953. However, in 1924, fellow climbers thought they saw two climbers named Mallory and Irvine who might of been near the summit. Than a mist covered Mallory and Irvine, and they were never seen again. In 1999, 75 years latter, a search party found Mallory's well-preserved body. His camera is still missing. The film in it could lie the mystery to rest once and for all.

WEEK 22: **Corrected Paragraph**

Were Sir Edmund Hillary and Tenzing Norgay_∧his guide_∧the first to reach the top of Mt. Everest_/?_They reached the summit on May 29_∧1953. However, in 1924, fellow climbers thought they saw two climbers named Mallory and Irvine who might ~~of~~ *have* been near the summit. ~~Than~~ *Then* a mist covered Mallory and Irvine, and they were never seen again. In 1999, 75 years ~~latter~~ *later*, a search party found Mallory's well-preserved body. His camera is still missing. The film in it could ~~lie~~ *lay* the mystery to rest once and for all.

WEEK 23: It's Only Ice

- **Capitalization, Verb (Irregular), Sentence Fragment, Period, Double Subjects**

In 1909, Robert e Peary and Matthew A. Henson reached the north axis of the world. Well, there is no santa claus at the north pole, and there is no actual pole at the north pole! The pair of explorers finded there is not even land up there. Everything is ice, ice, ice. It's dangerous. Because the ice cracks frequently. Luckily, the men they got back before they floated out to sea on an iceberg.

WEEK 23: **Corrected Paragraph**

In 1909, Robert ⟨E.⟩ Peary and Matthew A. Henson reached the north axis of the world. Well, there is no ⟨S⟩anta ⟨C⟩laus at the ⟨N⟩orth ⟨P⟩ole, and there is no actual pole at the ⟨N⟩orth ⟨P⟩ole! The pair of explorers ~~finded~~ *found* there is not even land up there. Everything is ice, ice, ice. It's dangerous⟨.⟩ ⟨B⟩ecause the ice cracks frequently. Luckily, the men ~~they~~ got back before they floated out to sea on an iceberg.

WEEK 24: The Sky-High Sears Tower

- **Comma (To Keep Numbers Clear and To Set Off Introductory Phrases and Clauses), Subject-Verb Agreement, Adjective (Comparative/Superlative), Capitalization**

At 1450 feet the sears tower in Chicago is the most tallest building in the whole United States. Some people says the building looks like stacks of catalogs. That shouldn't surprise anyone. The Sears Tower were built to hold the offices of Sears, roebuck and Company, the most biggest catalog company in the world. On a clear day you can see 80 miles in any direction if you're brave enough to go to the top of the Sears Tower.

WEEK 24: **Corrected Paragraph**

At 1,450 feet, the **S**ears **T**ower in Chicago is the ~~most~~ tallest building in the whole United States. Some people ~~says~~ *say* the building looks like stacks of catalogs. That shouldn't surprise anyone. The Sears Tower ~~were~~ *was* built to hold the offices of Sears, **R**oebuck and Company, the ~~most~~ biggest catalog company in the world. On a clear day, you can see 80 miles in any direction if you're brave enough to go to the top of the Sears Tower.

WEEK 25: Brasília Is Booming

■ **Using the Right Word, Comma (Between Two Independent Clauses), Numbers, Run-On Sentence**

The capitol of Brazil is only forty years old. That's young for a capital city. Brazil's capital was located in Rio de Janeiro but in 1960 the capital was moved from the coast far into the Brazilian jungle. At first, people laughed they said nobody would ever want to live in Brasília. They were wrong Brasília now has close to 2,000,000 people.

WEEK 25: **Corrected Paragraph** (Answers may vary.)

The ~~capitol~~ *capital* of Brazil is only ~~forty~~ *40* years old. That's young for a capital city. Brazil's capital was located in Rio de Janeiro*,* but in 1960 the capital was moved from the coast far into the Brazilian jungle. At first, people laughed*. T*hey said nobody would ever want to live in Brasília. They were wrong*.* Brasília now has close to ~~2,000,000~~ *2 million* people.

WEEK 26: The "Boneshaker"

■ **Comma (To Set Off Appositives), Pronoun-Antecedent Agreement, Subject-Verb Agreement, Sentence Problems ("Of" for "Have"), Double Subjects**

The velocipede an early bicycle was popular in France in the 1860s. Its frame and wheels were made of wood. Their tires were iron. This early bicycle it were called the "boneshaker" in England. That's how it would of felt to ride the thing on rough roads or cobblestone streets. Bikers in the late 1800s spoke out for better roads. Then when better roads came along, bicycles they was pretty much left in the dust.

WEEK 26: **Corrected Paragraph**

The velocipede ˄ an early bicycle ˄ was popular in France in the 1860s.
                    /,\   /,\
                                                        Its
Its frame and wheels were made of wood. ~~Their~~ tires were iron. This
                                was
early bicycle ~~it were~~ called the "boneshaker" in England. That's how it
        have
would ~~of~~ felt to ride the thing on rough roads or cobblestone streets.

Bikers in the late 1800s spoke out for better roads. Then when better
                                        were
roads came along, bicycles ~~they was~~ pretty much left in the dust.

WEEK 27: Everyone's Uncle

■ **Comma (To Set Off Interruptions), Quotation Marks, Subject-Verb Agreement, Capitalization, Apostrophe (In Possessives), Plurals**

He's your Uncle. he's my uncle. he's everybodys uncle—uncle Sam! You've seen pictures of him dressed up in the stares and stripes, wearing a top hat, pointing a bony finger straight out, and saying, Uncle Sam Wants You! He may have been named after a character in an 1787 play called *The Contrast,* but his name in case you are wondering come from the initials for our country—U.S.

WEEK 27: **Corrected Paragraph**

He's your ~~U~~**u**ncle. **H**~~h~~e's my uncle. **H**~~h~~e's everybody**'**s uncle—**U**~~u~~ncle Sam! You've seen pictures of him dressed up in the ~~stares~~ **stars** and stripes, wearing a top hat, pointing a bony finger straight out, and saying,**"**Uncle Sam Wants You!**"** He may have been named after a character in an 1787 play called *The Contrast,* but his name**,** in case you are wondering**,** ~~come~~ **comes** from the initials for our country—U.S.

WEEK 28: The Power of Light

■ **Quotation Marks (Special Words), Apostrophe (In Contractions), Colon, Comma (Items in a Series), End Punctuation**

The word *laser* is an acronym that stands for light amplification by stimulated emission of radiation. What a mouthful. To make things simple, lets just say that lasers are superbright, powerful light beams. Youve seen them in space movies, but in real life they can do the following drill holes in diamonds, speed up communications—both on earth and in space and help doctors perform "bloodless" surgery.

WEEK 28: **Corrected Paragraph**

The word *laser* is an acronym that stands for "light amplification by stimulated emission of radiation." What a mouthful! To make things simple, let's just say that lasers are superbright, powerful light beams. You've seen them in space movies, but in real life they can do the following: drill holes in diamonds, speed up communications—both on earth and in space, and help doctors perform "bloodless" surgery.

WEEK 29: Your Fingerprints Do the Talking

■ **Comma (Between Two Independent Clauses), Pronoun-Antecedent Agreement, Subject-Verb Agreement, Run-On Sentence, Verb (Irregular)**

The tiny ridges found on your fingertips form patterns called "fingerprints." Like snowflakes, no two sets of fingerprints is identical. Your fingerprints do not change you can be identified by them throughout your life. The British first taked and used fingerprints in India to identify criminals in the 1890s. Today, computers can digitally record fingerprints and send it anywhere. You are not your fingerprints but your fingerprints are always you.

WEEK 29: **Corrected Paragraph** (Answers may vary.)

The tiny ridges found on your fingertips form patterns called
                                                            are
"fingerprints." Like snowflakes, no two sets of fingerprints ~~is~~ identical.
                                            Y
Your fingerprints do not change. You can be identified by them throughout
                              took
your life. The British first ~~taked~~ and used fingerprints in India to
identify criminals in the 1890s. Today, computers can digitally record
                        them
fingerprints and send ~~it~~ anywhere. You are not your fingerprints, but
your fingerprints are always you.

WEEK 30: Times Do Change

■ **Numbers, Comma (To Set Off Introductory Phrases and Clauses), Capitalization, Verb (Irregular)**

Charlene Hunter-Gault was the first african American female student at the university of georgia in 1962. Guards brought her to school. A brick and a bottle were thrown through her dormitory window. Hunter-Gault became a well-respected journalist. She was on pbs for 20 years and winned just about every award out there. 35 years after graduating from the school she almost didn't get into she was invited back to give the graduation speech.

WEEK 30: **Corrected Paragraph**

Charlene Hunter-Gault was the first *A*/african American female student at the *U*/university of *G*/georgia in 1962. Guards brought her to school. A brick and a bottle were thrown through her dormitory window. Hunter-Gault became a well-respected journalist. She was on ~~pbs~~ *PBS* for 20 years and ~~winned~~ *won* just about every award out there. ~~35~~ *Thirty-five* years after graduating from the school she almost didn't get into*,* she was invited back to give the graduation speech.

WEEK 31: Dancing the Charleston

■ **Comma (In Addresses), Capitalization, Run-On Sentence, Verb (Irregular), Using the Right Word, Apostrophe (In Possessives)**

Have you ever seed anyone do the Charleston? Its an American dance that can be performed as a solo, with a partner, or in a group. You don't have to be knock-kneed too do the Charleston, but it helps. You also need to kick up your legs and fling you're arms around alot. The Charleston comes from Charleston south Carolina ware it was a African American folk dance the Charleston was everybodys dance in the 1920s.

WEEK 31: Corrected Paragraph

Have you ever ~~seed~~ *seen* anyone do the Charleston? ~~Its~~ *It's* an American dance that can be performed as a solo, with a partner, or in a group. You don't have to be knock-kneed ~~too~~ *to* do the Charleston, but it helps. You also need to kick up your legs and fling ~~you're~~ *your* arms around ~~alot~~ *a lot*. The Charleston comes from Charleston*,* *S*outh Carolina*,* ~~ware~~ *where* it was ~~a~~ *an* African American folk dance*.* *T*he Charleston was everybody*'*s dance in the 1920s.

WEEK 32: A Nobel Family

- **Comma (Items in a Series, In Addresses, and To Set Off Interruptions), Sentence Fragment, Numbers, Abbreviations**

   Marie Curie graduated 1st in her class at the Sorbonne, a famous school in Paris Fr. Marie, her husband her daughter and her daughter's husband were all physicists. They all received Nobel Prizes in physics or chemistry. That's pretty amazing. Because the Nobel Prize is the top prize in the whole world. Marie in fact received 2 Nobel Prizes, one with her husband and the 2nd one many years after his death.

WEEK 32: Corrected Paragraph

   Marie Curie graduated ~~1st~~ *first* in her class at the Sorbonne, a famous school in Paris, *France* ~~Fr.~~ Marie, her husband, her daughter, and her daughter's husband were all physicists. They all received Nobel Prizes in physics or chemistry. That's pretty amazing, because the Nobel Prize is the top prize in the whole world. Marie, in fact, received *two* ~~2~~ Nobel Prizes, one with her husband and the *second* ~~2nd~~ one many years after his death.

WEEK 33: Go Nuts

■ **Comma (To Set Off Interjections and Between Two Independent Clauses), Pronoun-Antecedent Agreement, Double Negatives, End Punctuation**

Do you know how hard it is to stop eating peanuts! Well George Washington Carver couldn't stop thinking of ways to use peanuts. He kept going until they had invented more than 300 uses for peanuts. Carver wanted to help Southern farmers grow something besides cotton, for it wears out the soil. He invented many other things as well but Carver never held no patent on any of his inventions.

WEEK 33: **Corrected Paragraph**

Do you know how hard it is to stop eating peanuts! Well George Washington Carver couldn't stop thinking of ways to use peanuts. He kept going until ~~they~~ *he* had invented more than 300 uses for peanuts. Carver wanted to help Southern farmers grow something besides cotton, for it wears out the soil. He invented many other things as well but Carver never held ~~no~~ *a* patent on any of his inventions.

WEEK 34: Sounds of Music

- **Comma (Items in a Series and To Set Off Introductory Phrases and Clauses), Using the Right Word, Subject-Verb Agreement, Spelling**

Imagine a time when there was no radios tape decks or CD players. If you wanted to here music you had to create it yourself or listen to someone else play an instrument or sing. The first phonograph records was made of heavy, breakable shellac. Then vinyl records was a big improvment. Than came tapes and CD's. Music had become portable, and life has never been the same.

WEEK 34: **Corrected Paragraph**

Imagine a time when there ~~was~~ *were* no radios, tape decks, or CD players. If you wanted to ~~here~~ *hear* music, you had to create it yourself or listen to someone else play an instrument or sing. The first phonograph records ~~was~~ *were* made of heavy, breakable shellac. Then vinyl records ~~was~~ *were* a big ~~improvment.~~ *improvement* ~~Than~~ *Then* came tapes and CD's. Music had become portable, and life has never been the same.

WEEK 35: King Kong

■ **Italics and Underlining, Hyphen, Using the Right Word, Quotation Marks, Capitalization, Comma (In Direct Address)**

King Kong is perhaps the most famous monster movie of all time. It was an immediate hit when the 100 minute movie was shown for the first time in 1933. On the screen, the giant ape was 24 feet high. In real life, Kong was an 18 inch model covered with rabbit hare. My Grandma said, Jerry I can't ever see the empire state building without imagining that hairy monster clinging to it's top.

WEEK 35: **Corrected Paragraph**

<u>King Kong</u> is perhaps the most famous monster movie of all time. It was an immediate hit when the 100-minute movie was shown for the first time in 1933. On the screen, the giant ape was 24 feet high. In real life, Kong was an 18-inch model covered with rabbit *hair* hare. My Grandma said, "Jerry, I can't ever see the *E*mpire *S*tate *B*uilding without imagining that hairy monster clinging to *its* it's top."

Daily Writing Practice

This section offers three types of writing practice. The freewriting done in response to the **writing prompts** can be shared in follow-up sessions and later shaped into finished narratives or essays. The discussion of daily journal writing introduces lists of **writing topics.** The topics address a wide range of writing ideas. Finally "showing" in writing, developed by expanding on the **Show-Me sentences,** can be shared in follow-up sessions and later shaped into finished descriptive paragraphs.

Writing Prompts
A Writing Prompts FAQ Sheet

You may duplicate the following question-and-answer information about writing prompts as a handout for students or use it as the basis for a class discussion.

Anyone who wants to be a good writer has to practice often. That's why so many writers keep journals and diaries. And that's why your teacher asks you to write something nearly every day in school. Your teacher may ask you to write about a specific topic or about a personal experience. Your teacher might also ask you to use a writing prompt.

A writing prompt can be anything from a question to a photograph to a quotation. The idea is for you to write whatever you can without planning or researching the topic. You simply write what you have inside. And you keep writing until all your thoughts are gone. That's it!

How do I get started? It's really very simple. You just write down whatever comes into your mind when you think about your writing prompt. This doesn't have to be much. All you are looking for is an idea to get you going.

Shouldn't I plan out what I'm going to write about? No, you shouldn't plan anything. That's the whole idea. Just write. You don't need to know where your writing will take you. Mystery is good; in fact, it is the mystery and surprises along the way that get writers hooked on writing.

What can I do to keep my writing going? Don't stop! When you run out of ideas, shift gears and try writing about your topic in a slightly different way. For example, you might compare your topic to something else. Or you might use dialogue between two or more people who are discussing your topic. Or you might think of a specific audience—like a group of first graders—and write so they can understand your topic. Whatever you do, keep the ideas flowing as freely as possible.

When should I stop? If you are doing a timed writing (3, 5, or 10 minutes), stop when the time is up. You might decide it's time to stop when you've filled up the entire page. (Or you might keep going, using another sheet of paper.) Or you might decide to stop when you feel that you've done as much thinking and writing as you can and your brain is drained.

What do I do with my writing? You might share it with a classmate and see what she or he thinks. Or you might turn your writing into a more polished essay, story, or poem. Or you might set it aside and use it later when you need a topic for a writing assignment.

So, really, all I have to do is start writing? Right!

WRITING PROMPT

How would the world look if I were the size of a butterfly?

_____

_____

_____

_____

_____

_____

_____

_____

_____

_____

_____

_____

_____

WRITING PROMPT

The day
I was born . . .

WRITING PROMPT

We found ourselves in a thicket.

WRITING PROMPT

I had never seen . . .

_____

_____

_____

_____

_____

_____

WRITING PROMPT

The Land of Plenty

WRITING PROMPT
Another Challenge

_____

_____

_____

_____

_____

_____

_____

_____

_____

_____

_____

_____

_____

WRITING PROMPT

The last time I went to the doctor's office . . .

_____

_____

_____

_____

_____

_____

_____

_____

_____

_____

_____

_____

_____

WRITING PROMPT

The only light came from a dim streetlamp.

WRITING PROMPT

The gorilla didn't look happy.

_____

_____

_____

_____

_____

_____

_____

_____

_____

_____

_____

_____

_____

_____

WRITING PROMPT

Our cruise ship is leaving for . . .

WRITING PROMPT

I will never forget . . .

_____

_____

_____

_____

_____

_____

_____

_____

_____

_____

_____

_____

_____

WRITING PROMPT **(Write your own.)**

WRITING PROMPT

When we realized we were shipwrecked . . .

_____

_____

_____

_____

_____

_____

_____

_____

_____

_____

_____

_____

_____

WRITING PROMPT

I think I'd like to try that sometime.

WRITING PROMPT

A Day in the Country

_____

_____

_____

_____

_____

_____

_____

_____

_____

_____

_____

_____

_____

WRITING PROMPT

Home, Sweet Home!

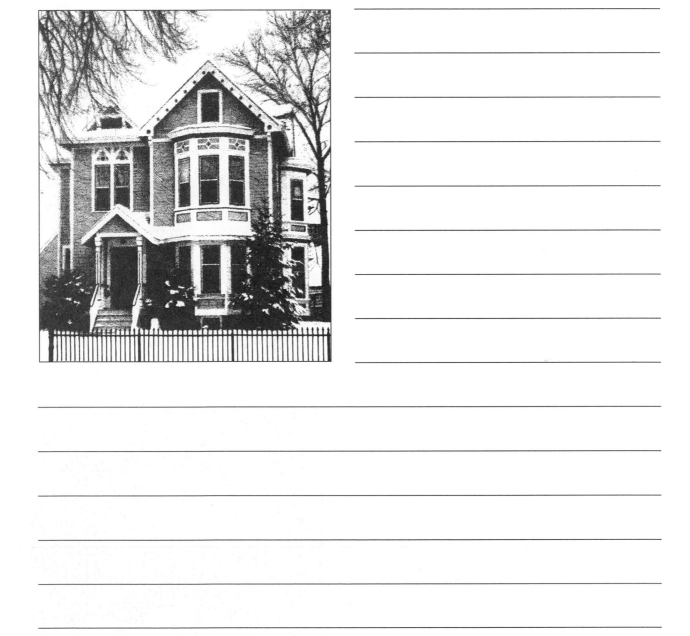

WRITING PROMPT

At the end of the rainbow . . .

_____

_____

_____

_____

_____

_____

_____

_____

_____

_____

_____

_____

_____

_____

Writing Topics
Daily Journal Writing

> "I can tap into [my students'] human instinct to write if I help them realize that their lives and memories are worth telling stories about, and if I help them zoom in on topics of fundamental importance to them."
>
> **—writing teacher JUNE GOULD**

As classroom teachers, we know from firsthand experience that the personal stories young learners love to share can serve as the basis of an effective and lively writing program. Here's how we did it:

Getting Started

At the beginning of the school year, we introduced in-class journal writing to the students. (We encouraged them to write outside of class in journals as well, but the journals in school were part of our writing program.) We knew that the most effective way to get students into writing was simply to let them write often and freely about their own lives, without having to worry about grades or turning their writing in. This helped them develop a feel for "real" writing—writing that originates from their own thoughts and feelings.

That's where the journals come in. Nothing gets students into writing more effectively than a personal journal. (And no other type of writing is so easy to implement.) All your students need are spiral notebooks, pens, time to write, and encouragement to explore whatever is on their minds. (See page 133 in the *Writers Express* handbook for more information.)

We provided our students with four or five personal writing topics each time they wrote. They could use one of these topics as a starting point, or write about something else entirely. The choice was theirs. (We found that providing writing topics was easier and more productive than just saying "You've got plenty to write about.")

Writing Topics

To start off an exercise, we posted suggested writing topics like these:

- your most memorable kitchen-related experience,
- coping with brothers or sisters,
- being home alone, late at night, or
- what you did over the weekend.

Students would either choose from the list or write on a topic they preferred. See pages 141-144 in this booklet for more suggested topics. We asked our students to write every other day for the first 10 minutes of the class period. (Every Monday, Wednesday, and Friday were writing days.) Of course, we had to adjust our schedule at times, but, for the most part, the students wrote three times a week.

Keeping It Going

After everyone was seated and roll was taken, the journals were passed out, the topics were given, and everyone wrote. We expected students to write for a full 10 minutes, nonstop. They knew that they would earn a quarterly journal grade based on the number of words they produced. This almost made a contest out of the writing sessions. Each time they wrote, they wanted to see if they could increase their production from past journal entries, and they always wanted to write more than their classmates.

> "Over the last fifteen years, a number of teachers around the country and their students have been amazed by what happened when people write ten to fifteen minutes without worrying about grammar, spelling, or punctuation, and concentrate only on telling some kind of truth."
>
> —KEN MACRORIE

Wrapping It Up

On days that we weren't writing, we shared journal entries. First, each student would exchange journals with a classmate. He or she would count the number of words in the latest entry, read it carefully, and then make comments on things he or she liked or questioned. After each pair had shared their comments with one another, we would talk about the entries as a class.

Many writers themselves would be reluctant to share their entries with the entire class. But the readers had no problem volunteering someone else's entry ("You've got to hear Nick's story") and reading it out loud. The students loved these readings and the discussions that followed.

Personal Experience Papers

Periodically, we would interrupt the normal course of journal writing and sharing and make formal writing assignments. That is, we would ask students to review their entries and select one (or part of one) to develop into a more polished, complete, personal experience paper. Usually, those entries that readers enjoyed and wanted to know more about would be the ones the young writers would choose to develop.

We wanted to make sure that their writing went through at least one or two thorough revisions, so we gave our writers plenty of class time to work on their papers. We also required them to turn in all preliminary work with their final drafts. (See "Writing Personal Narratives," page 138, in the *Writers Express* handbook for guidelines for this type of writing.)

The experience papers were shared with the entire class at the end of the project. This was a fun and informal activity, but one that students came to appreciate as an important part of the entire composing process. It was their day. They were on stage. They were sharing the culmination of all their hard work—a special moment in their own lives.

Writing Topics

Titles

- Lost in the Supermarket
- The Fortune Cookie
- The Microwave Accident
- Grandpa's Garden
- Fearsome Frank

If . . .

- If I were rich . . .
- If I were a giant . . .
- If I could see the future . . .
- If I could help anyone or any group of people . . .
- If I could meet a celebrity . . .

How?

- How can there be water shortages when water covers more than 70 percent of the earth's surface?
- How could I have been such a fool?
- How can I show my parents that I appreciate them?
- How do people get over a bad experience?
- How does a magician think of tricks?

Why?

- Why does singing make me feel better?
- Why don't people treat each other with more respect?
- Why not have school year-round, with several short vacations instead of one long summer vacation?
- Why is money such a big part of life for adults?

Playing Games

- The sport that's most fun to play
- The sport that's most fun to watch
- A board game that teaches me something
- Made-up games we used to play
- Competing
- Winning
- Losing
- Team sports vs. individual sports
- My favorite game

Writing Topics

Variety

- A person is old when . . .
- The importance of volunteering
- A raw deal
- The storm I remember
- Someone who is "spoiled rotten"
- Looking at a sky full of stars, I think . . .
- The best time of the year

Friends and Schoolmates

- A good time with my friends
- A kid in school I admire
- Passing notes
- Riding the bus on a field trip
- Valentine's Day
- Sleepovers
- Recess

Self-Centered

- My ideal birthday feast
- My room is . . .
- When I am happy, I . . .
- Even though my parents won't permit it, I think I deserve . . .
- When I have time to myself, I . . .
- I get bored when . . .
- I showed my bravery . . .
- My favorite TV show
- The color I like best
- What I do best
- My best time of day
- My idea of fun
- I feel at peace when . . .
- I want to be more . . .
- My idea of a great job
- My favorite photograph

Writing Topics

Endings

- It all comes to this . . .
- One more thing . . .
- My last point . . .
- To sum it all up . . .
- There's just one problem . . .
- For the last time . . .
- Just remember . . .
- On the other side . . .
- I was wrong about . . .
- Would you believe?

Dialogues Between . . .

- Two women/two men
- Two kindergartners
- Two teachers
- Two parents
- A brother and a sister
- A child and a grandparent
- A child and a friend
- Two teammates
- Two animals
- Two pieces of furniture
- Two cars

Character Sketches

- Oldest person
- Strongest person
- Bravest person
- Favorite teacher
- Hero (TV or movie)
- Character from literature
- Hardest worker
- Person I admire most
- Interesting character
- Favorite relative

Explaining Things

- How to bake . . .
- How to build a . . .
- How to play . . .
- How to write . . .
- How to plan . . .
- How to teach . . .
- How to eat . . .
- How to grow . . .

Writing Topics

Observing

- People at work
- People at play
- Pets
- Animals in the wild
- Sunrises and sunsets
- Gardens
- City streets
- Country scenes
- Barnyards
- Schoolyards
- Sporting events
- Circuses
- Nature

Sound Effects

- Rushing water
- Thunder and lightning
- Music
- Traffic noises
- Around the house
- Night sounds
- Sirens and alarms
- Birds

Teamwork

- As a family
- As a neighborhood
- In the classroom
- On a trip
- At camp
- Playing sports
- With friends

What I've learned about . . .

- Love
- Trust
- Fear
- Hope
- Kindness
- Truth
- Life
- Friendship
- Anger
- Disappointment
- Success
- Change

Show-Me Sentences
Producing Writing with Detail

From time immemorial teachers have said to their students, "Your essay lacks details" or "This idea is too general" or "Show, don't tell." We even know of a teacher who had a special stamp made: "Give more examples."

So how should this problem be approached? It's obvious that simply telling students to add more details and examples is not enough. Even showing them how professional writers develop their ideas is not enough (although this does help). Students learn to add substance and depth to their writing through regular practice.

Here's one method that has worked for many students and teachers: the Show-Me sentences. Students begin with a basic topic—"My locker is messy," for example—and create a paragraph or brief essay that *shows* rather than *tells*. The sentence is a springboard for lively writing.

About Your Show-Me Sentences . . .

The following pages contain 45 Show-Me sentences. Each sentence speaks directly to students, so they should have little difficulty creating essays full of personal details. Again, we suggest that you use these sentences every other day for an extended period of time (at least a month).

Note: By design, each page of Show-Me sentences can be made into an overhead transparency.

Implementation

DAY ONE Before you ask students to work on their own, develop a Show-Me sentence as a class. Start by writing a sample sentence on the board. Then have students volunteer specific details that give this basic thought some life. List their ideas on the board. Next, construct a brief paragraph on the board using some of these details. (Make no mention of the original sentence in your paragraph.) Discuss the results. Make sure that your students see how specific details help create a visual image for the reader. Also have your students read and react to examples of "showing writing" from professional texts. (Share the sample of "showing writing" on page 147 with your students.)

DAY TWO Have students work on their first Show-Me sentences in class. Upon completion of their writing, have pairs of students share the results of their work. Then ask for volunteers to share their writing with the entire class. (Make copies of strong writing for future class discussions.)

DAY THREE Ask students to develop a new paragraph. At the beginning of the *next* class period, discuss the results (break into pairs as before). Continue in this fashion for at least a month.

Note: Reserve the first 5 or 10 minutes of each class period for writing or discussing. (Students who don't finish their writing in class should have it ready for the next day.)

Evaluation

Have students reserve a section in their notebooks for their writing or have them compile their work in a folder. At regular intervals, give them some type of performance score for their efforts. At the end of the unit, have them select one or two of their best examples to revise and then submit for a thorough evaluation.

Enrichment

In *Writers in Training,* Rebekah Caplan developed an extensive program to help students produce well-detailed, engaging essays. She made the following suggestions:

- Have your students turn cliches like *It's a small world* or *Accidents will happen* into strong narrative or descriptive paragraphs.

- Have them develop sentences like *Friday nights are better than Saturday nights* into paragraphs that compare and contrast two subjects.

- In addition, have students convert loaded statements like *Noon hours are too short* or *I don't need a bedtime* into opinion pieces.

Note: In a sense, these variations become progressively more challenging. Most student writers, for example, have more difficulty supporting an opinion than they have illustrating the basic ideas behind a cliche.

- You might also use vocabulary words from science, math, social studies, and so forth, in Show-Me sentences or connect these sentences to literary works under study. (Generally speaking, Show-Me sentences can be linked to any unit of study.)

Sample Showing Writing

■ **On the dance floor, Dad is like a fish out of water.** *(cliche)*

On the dance floor, Dad has absolutely no sense of rhythm. He can't remember even the simplest dance steps. He'll do twists and spins and just move his arms and feet, and this, to him, is dancing. His limbs keep popping up at strange times. He tries to move to the music, but it looks as though he is fighting with it. He just wants to have fun, though, like everyone else—and he does!

SHOW-ME SENTENCES

- **It looks like a storm is coming.**

- **Breakfast is the most important meal of the day.**

- **Dirty streets make our city look bad.**

- **The size of the job discouraged me.**

- **It's hard to remember to do my homework sometimes.**

SHOW-ME SENTENCES

■ **I miss my _____.**

■ **She is such a shy girl.**

■ **I was shocked at how different he looked.**

■ **It is unfair that we get only half an hour for recess.**

■ **I wish I could get a new bike.**

SHOW-ME SENTENCES

■ **It felt as though we had been driving for days.**

■ **I don't like how I look in this picture.**

■ **He was big and clumsy.**

■ **Chimpanzees are interesting.**

■ **We all felt a chill when the lights went out.**

SHOW-ME SENTENCES

- **She made a mistake.**

- **The fire was incredibly bright.**

- **I really dislike insects.**

- **His Halloween mask was frightening.**

- **The United States is a privileged nation.**

SHOW-ME SENTENCES

- **He was getting tired of his little brother.**

- **I worry about _____ .**

- **She is a big basketball fan.**

- **We were disappointed.**

- **Some people do not get wiser with age.**

SHOW-ME SENTENCES

■ **He was lucky to walk away from it without a scratch.**

■ **Those two argue way too much.**

■ **I was happy as could be.**

■ **There's no place like home.**

■ **Some of us think she is too sensitive.**

SHOW-ME SENTENCES

■ **Music has magical powers.**

■ **I've been feeling crummy all day.**

■ **Playing video games has affected him.**

■ **I was so surprised.**

■ **We just made the bus.**

SHOW-ME SENTENCES

- **Dogs are more friendly than cats.**

- **She's a smart woman.**

- **You should be proud of yourself.**

- **I value your friendship.**

- **He has many good qualities.**

SHOW-ME SENTENCES

- **This place is in sad shape.**

- **He is a genius in the kitchen.**

- **That elderly person seems lonely.**

- **She needs a more positive attitude.**

- **He said he just lost his head.**